Introduction

Big Book of Basic Skills

GRADE 2

Now you can have a wonderful variety of exciting and challenging activities for your students to do right at your fingertips! This *Big Book of Basic Skills* is packed with activities that are divided into nine chapters—Manuscript Handwriting, Phonics, Grammar, Mechanics, Spelling, Vocabulary Development, Reading Comprehension, Choral Reading, and Math.

Each chapter features age-appropriate activities that students will find interesting, relevant, and challenging. In many of the chapters, the activities build upon one another and enable students to continuously add to their existing knowledge and learn to apply new skills and concepts. The activities provide a wonderful supplement to all kinds of programs that exist in the nine subject areas listed above.

The activities featured include a wide variety of formats thus allowing every child to be successful and to gain a great sense of accomplishment. Most of the pages include extension ideas that provide more stimulating and challenging activities for those children who want more knowledge on a particular topic or more practice with a specific skill. An answer key is also provided at the back of the book.

Below and on page 2 is a brief overview of the contents of each chapter.

▼ Chapter 1, *Manuscript Handwriting*, helps students learn to write the letters of the alphabet. Each letter is featured on its own page. Students can trace its uppercase and lowercase forms and then practice writing the letters on their own. Also on each page are two sentences featuring the designated letter. Students are provided the opportunities to trace and write these as well. Activities involving the writing of numerals, the days of the week, the months of the year, and a list of words which together contain all the letters of the alphabet can be found on pages 31–34.

▼ Chapter 2, *Phonics,* is filled with wonderful phonics activities students can complete to help them become better spellers and readers. The activities have been designed to promote students' learning of vowels and vowel sounds, blends, digraphs, diphthongs, soft and hard consonant sounds, silent letters, double consonants, and much more. By completing these activities, you and the students will be thrilled as they gain confidence while developing important listening, speaking, reading, and writing skills.

FS-32502 Big Book of Basic Skills

▼ Chapter 3, *Grammar*, contains all the necessary skills students need to learn in order to have good grammar. Students will enjoy unscrambling sentences, coloring, matching, working puzzles, and more as they learn to identify sentences, use a variety of different parts of speech, and form plural nouns, among many other skills.

▼ Chapter 4, *Mechanics*, has been designed to help students learn, practice, and feel confident about the language mechanics skills involving capitalization and punctuation. Each skill begins with rules and examples which are followed by practice. Review pages are also provided at the end of the chapter so students can see how well they have understood the skills presented.

▼ Chapter 5, *Spelling*, is filled with activities that will enable students to become much more proficient spellers. Each activity page features a list of spelling words and activities involving all of the words. Also provided on page 128 are suggestions you can use to present students with a complete spelling program.

▼ Chapter 6, *Vocabulary Development*, features activities to help increase students' vocabularies and to develop in students a greater understanding and appreciation of the English language. Students will enjoy completing sentences, decoding messages, solving riddles, doing word searches, unscrambling words, and much more as they have fun increasing their vocabularies.

▼ Chapter 7, *Reading Comprehension*, provides a lot of stimulating stories and activities students can read and complete to learn how to better comprehend what they read. Some of the skills addressed include locating the main idea, recognizing details, sequencing, following directions, comparing and contrasting, and many more. You and the students will be pleasantly surprised as they come to recognize that reading is an enjoyable way to spend their time.

▼ Chapter 8, *Choral Reading*, helps students develop an appreciation for poetry. Poems of varying lengths are featured and provide students with opportunities to recite poems individually or in small or large groups. Students will enjoy reading poems aloud expressively as they learn how language is used at the same time.

▼ Chapter 9, *Math*, features activities that deal with basic math skills, including the concepts of time and money. Students are provided opportunities in this chapter to practice these math skills that will help them begin to understand many other mathematical properties that they will use every day of their lives.

This book enables teachers to easily help children learn many basic skills that play an important and valuable role in their lives.

CHAPTER 1

Manuscript Handwriting

Learning to write letters is an exciting and important task for students. It should be an enjoyable activity and one in which students experience success.

The activities presented in this chapter have been designed to help all students have fun as they learn to write the letters of the alphabet. Each letter is featured on its own page, and students are shown in steps how to write the letters. Students are then given the opportunity to trace each letter in its uppercase and lowercase forms and are provided with space they can use to practice writing the letters on their own.

Once students have practiced writing the letters, they can trace two sentences featuring each designated letter. Space is again provided for students to write each of these sentences. At the bottom of each page, a challenge relating to the letter is presented. Students can demonstrate their knowledge of each letter in their attempts at these activities.

Pages 31–34 contain activities students can do involving the writing of numerals, the days of the week, the months of the year, and a list of words which together contain all the letters of the alphabet. Combined with the previous letter pages, the activities presented in this chapter constitute a valuable resource for teachers wanting a fun, easy way to teach students how to write.

Fishing for Letters

Name _____

Aa　Bb　Cc　Dd

Ee　Ff　Gg　Hh

Ii　Jj　Kk　Ll

Mm　Nn　Oo　Pp

Qq　Rr　Ss　Tt

Uu　Vv　Ww　Xx

Yy　Zz

Try This! Write the alphabet backwards.

FS-32502 Big Book of Basic Skills

Name _____

Trace and write.

A   A

a   a

Aa   Aa

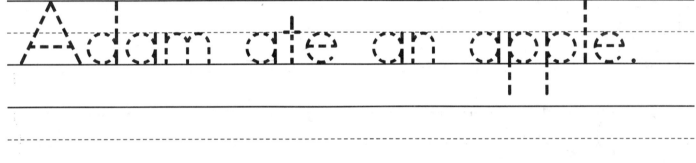

Adam ate an apple.

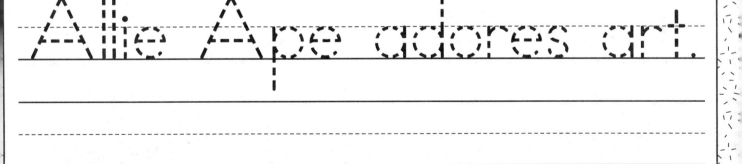

Allie Ape adores art.

 **Try This!**   Write your own sentence for the letter **a**.

Bb

Name _____

Trace and write.

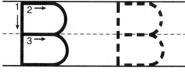

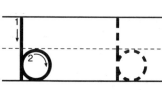

B b   B b

Bob baked bread.

Bees buzz busily.

 **Try This!** Write three words that begin with **b**.

FS-32502 Big Book of Basic Skills

Cc

Name _____

Trace and write.

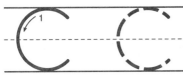

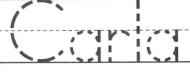 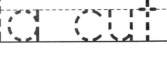

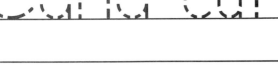

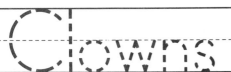

Try This! Write three names that begin with **C**.

FS-32502 Big Book of Basic Skills

Dd

Name _____

Trace and write.

D D D

d d d

Dd Dd

Did Dan dry dishes?

Do dogs dance?

⭐ **Try This!** Write a question beginning with **D**.

Ee

Ee

Name _____

Trace and write.

E E

e e

Ee Ee

Eagles excite Eddie.

Ellen enjoys eating.

Try This! Write a sentence about eels. Circle every **e**.

Ff

Name _____

Trace and write.

F F

f f

Ff Ff

Fran fed five frogs.

Fred Fox fried fish.

Try This! Write your own sentence for the letter **f**.

Gg

Name _____

Trace and write.

G   G

g   g

Gg   Gg

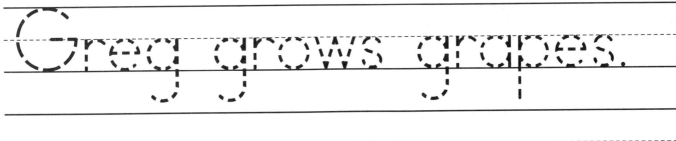

Greg grows grapes.

Geese gobble grain.

Try This!   Write three words that begin with **g**.

Hh

Name _____

Trace and write.

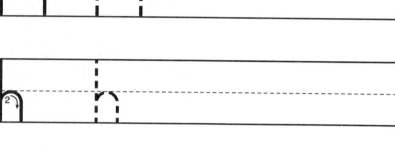

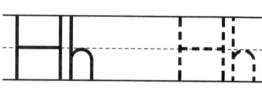

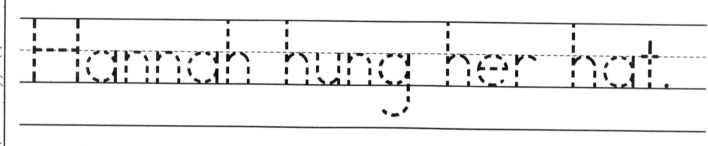

Hannah hung her hat.

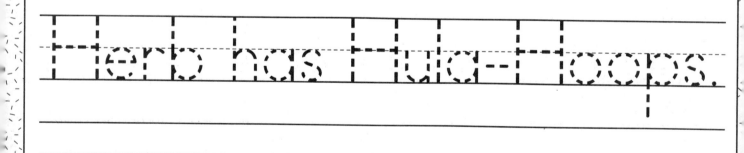

Herb has Hula-Hoops.

Try This! Write a sentence about horses. Circle every **h**.

12

FS-32502 Big Book of Basic Skills

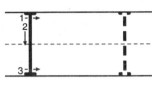

Ii

Name _____

Trace and write.

I

i

Ii   Ii

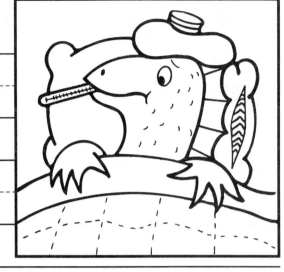

Irma is inviting Ian.

Iggy Iguana is ill.

Try This!   Write a question about icebergs. Circle every **i**.

© Frank Schaffer Publications, Inc.   13   FS-32502 Big Book of Basic Skills

Jj

Name _____

Trace and write.

J J J

j j j

J Jj Jj

Jan jumped joyfully.

Jays juggled jewels.

Try This! Write three names that begin with **J**.

Kk

Name _____

Trace and write.

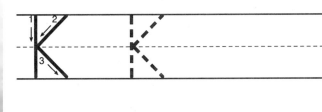

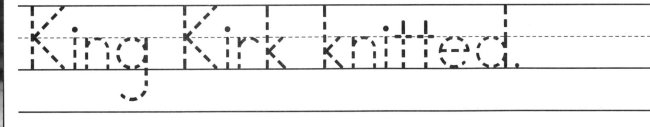

King Kirk knitted.

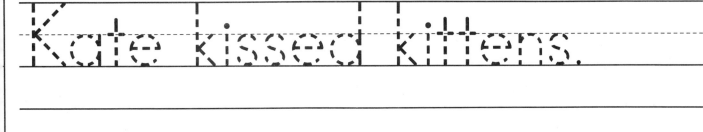

Kate kissed kittens.

Try This! Write three words that begin with **k**.

FS-32502 Big Book of Basic Skills

Ll

Name _____

Trace and write.

L

L

Ll   Ll

Lambs lick leaves.

Leo Lion likes lilies.

Try This! Write your own sentence for the letter l.

Mm

Name _____

Trace and write.

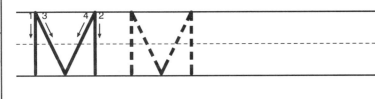

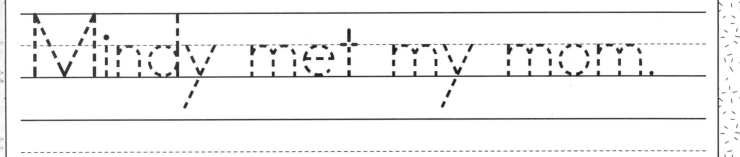

Mindy met my mom.

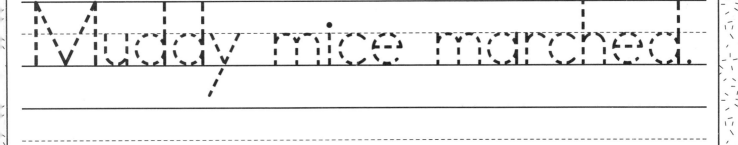

Muddy mice marched.

Try This! Write the names of three places that begin with **M**.

17

FS-32502 Big Book of Basic Skills

Name _____

Trace and write.

N N

n n

Nn Nn

Nurse Nancy napped.

Ned's newt nibbled.

Try This! Write three words that begin with **n**.

Name _____

Trace and write.

O   O

o   o

O o   O o

Oscar owns one ox.

Ollie ordered oranges.

Try This!   Write a sentence about an octopus. Circle every **o**.

Pp

Name ______________________________

Trace and write.

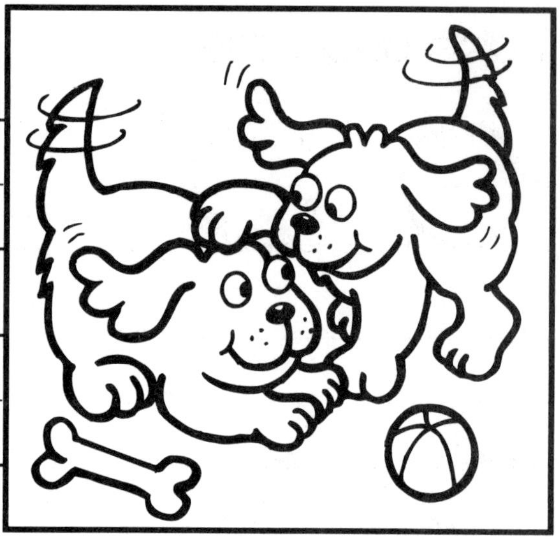

P P

p p

Pp Pp

Pam packed pajamas.

Perky puppies played.

Try This! Write your own sentence for the letter **p**.

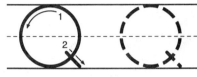

Name _____

Trace and write.

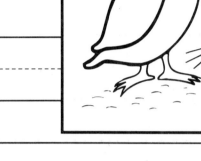

Qq Qq

Quentin quit quilting.

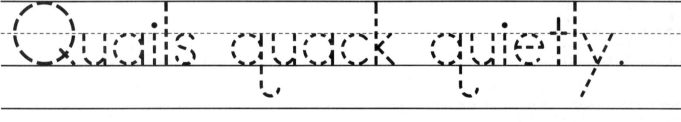

Quails quack quietly.

Try This!   Write a question about queens.

FS-32502 Big Book of Basic Skills

Name _____

Trace and write.

R R

r r

Rr Rr

Rats race rapidly.

Rob rides in rowboats.

Write three words that begin with **r**.

Name _____

Trace and write.

S S S

s s s

Ss Ss

Sue saw six swans.

Sally Seal sips soup.

 **Try This!** Write a sentence about school. Circle every **s**.

FS-32502 Big Book of Basic Skills

Tt

Name _____

Trace and write.

T T

t t

Tt Tt

Tim tapped the table.

Two tigers tasted tarts.

 Try This! Write the names of three places that begin with **T**.

Name _____

Trace and write.

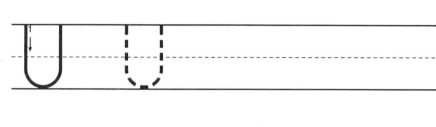

Unicorns upset Uri.

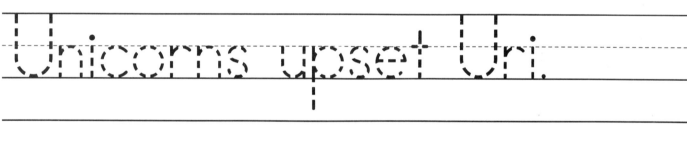

Una's uncle umpires.

 **Try This!** Write three words that begin with **u**.

Vv

Name ______________________________

Trace and write.

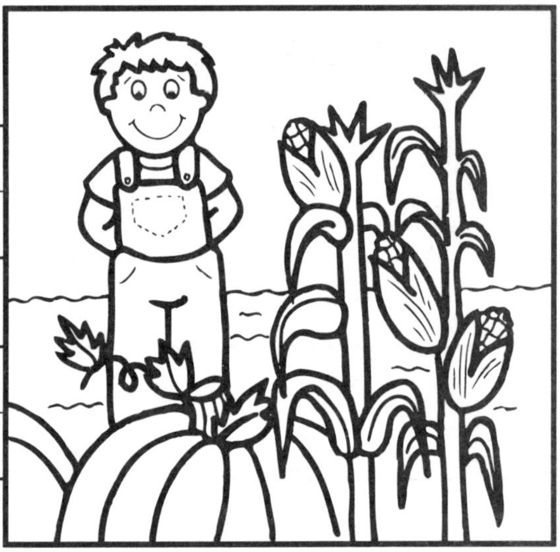

V V

v v

Vv Vv

Val's vacuum vibrates.

Vic views vegetables.

Try This! Write three words that contain **v**.

Name _____

Trace and write.

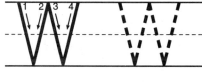

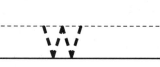

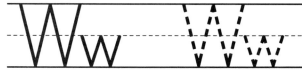

Wes washed windows.

Willy Worm wriggled.

Try This! Write your own sentence for the letter **w**.

Name _____

Trace and write.

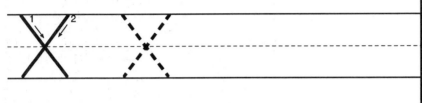

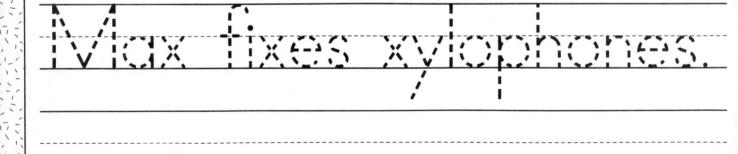

X-rays excite Rex.

Max fixes xylophones.

 **Try This!** Write three words that contain **x**.

FS-32502 Big Book of Basic Skills

Yy

Name _____

Trace and write.

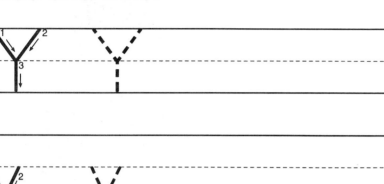

Yesterday yaks yelled.

Yvonne yanks yams.

Try This! Write a sentence telling what you did yesterday.

FS-32502 Big Book of Basic Skills

Name _____

Trace and write.

Z Z _____

Z z _____

Zz Zz

Zachary zooms by.

Zany zebras zigzag.

Write three words that contain **z.**

Number Trains

Name _____

Trace and write.

 Try This! Write how old you will be five years from now.

FS-32502 Big Book of Basic Skills

Days of the Week

Name _____

Write the days.

Try This! Write which day is your favorite and explain why.

32

Months of the Year

Name _____

Write the months.

January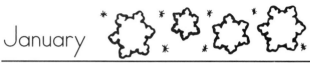

_____

- -

_____

February

_____

- -

_____

March

_____

- -

_____

April

_____

- -

_____

May

_____

- -

_____

June

_____

- -

_____

July

_____

- -

_____

August

_____

- -

_____

September

_____

- -

_____

October

_____

- -

_____

November

_____

- -

_____

December

_____

- -

_____

Try This! Write which month is your favorite and explain why.

FS-32502 Big Book of Basic Skills

Playtime Fun

Name _____

Copy this list of things to play with. The list contains every letter of the alphabet.

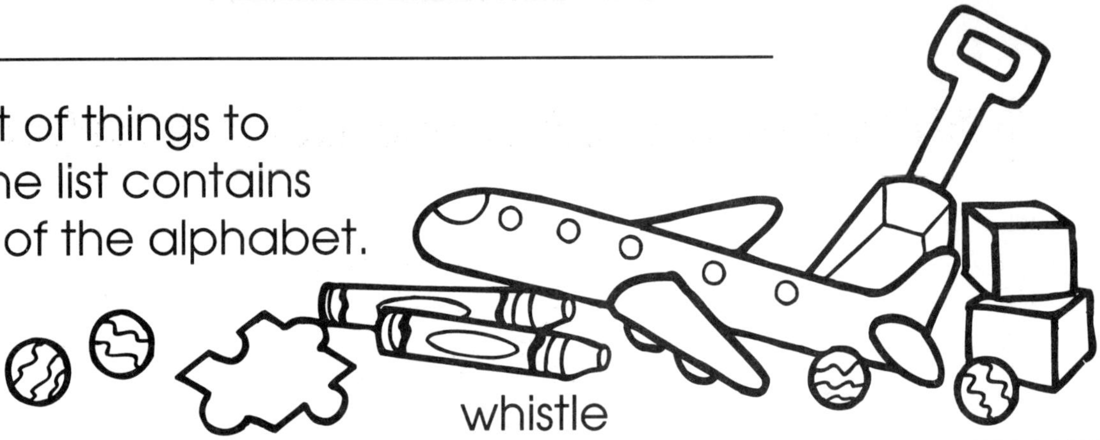

flag

jet

blocks

shovel

sandbox

whistle

crayon

puzzle

marbles

squirt gun

Try This! Make a list of three things you like to play with.

Introduction

CHAPTER 2

Phonics

By the time children have begun to read, they have already made great strides in mastering the basics of oral language. Their task, at this point, is to apply their knowledge to the written representation of language—reading and writing. This chapter provides students with the activities needed for them to accomplish this task.

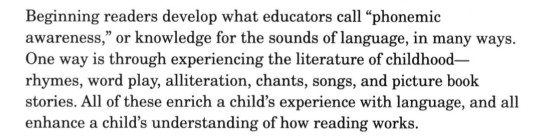

Beginning readers develop what educators call "phonemic awareness," or knowledge for the sounds of language, in many ways. One way is through experiencing the literature of childhood—rhymes, word play, alliteration, chants, songs, and picture book stories. All of these enrich a child's experience with language, and all enhance a child's understanding of how reading works.

This book has been designed to promote student learning of vowels and vowel sounds (short and long vowels, vowel combinations, etc.), final y, blends, digraphs, diphthongs, hard and soft consonant sounds, silent letters, double consonants, and much more. Through the completion of these activities, your students will experience success and therefore will gain confidence while developing listening, speaking, reading, and writing skills at the same time.

Camping Out

Name _____

Write the correct word for each sentence.

1. Dad and I like to _____ here.

   camp   send

2. We put up our _____ .

   ranch   tent

3. Then we looked at a _____ .

   help   map

4. We want to _____ fish.

   catch   pet

5. Where is the _____ place?

   best   back

6. Tomorrow we can go _____ .

   sack   west

7. I want to catch _____ fish.

   ten   fan

PHONICS

In the Kitchen

Name _____

Circle the short **i** words. (i)

Box the short **o** words. [o]

1. |Mom| likes to cook pancakes.

2. She uses a mix.

3. She reads the box.

4. She adds milk.

5. The mix gets thick.

6. The pan is hot.

7. The pancakes sizzle.

8. She lets me flip one.

9. I can have the big pancake.

10. It tastes good.

Summer Fun

Short u, e

Name _____

Print the missing vowels **u** or **e**. Write the words.

_____

_____

1. It is time to get _____p.

_____

2. The s_____n is hot today.

_____

3. B_____n wants to play.

_____

4. We get w_____t in the waves.

_____

5. That will be f_____n.

_____

6. Bring your toy tr_____ck.

_____

7. We can put sh_____lls in it.

_____

Crazy Caterpillar

Short vowels

Name _____

Say the name of each picture.
Write the vowel sound you hear.
Color the pictures.

Animal Riddles

Long vowels, silent e

Name _____

Fill in the correct vowel. Read the riddle.
Draw a line to the correct picture.

a   e   i   o   u

1. I am wh____te.

   I live on the ____ce.

2. I live in a c____ve.

   I have a m____ne.

3. See my white str____pe.

   Stay away from my h____me.

4. My baby likes to r____de.

   I swing on a v____ne.

5. I am h____ge.

   So is my n____se.

40

Vowel Search

Name _____

Circle the word
that names each
picture.

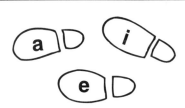

	mail mule mane	 fire fade fuse	 leak lake like
	rake ride rose	 tone tube tape	 more make mice
	whale wrote wide	 stripe stale stove	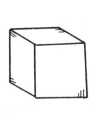 cube coal cave
	bone bike bake	 cane cute code	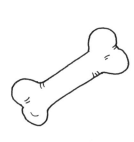 bale bone bite

FS-32502 Big Book of Basic Skills

Show You Know

Name _____

Say the name of each picture.
Write the vowel sound you hear.

| a e i o u |

c _ ke   t _ be   b _ ke

f _ re   b _ ne   wh _ el

c _ be   g _ me   b _ e

n _ se   tr _ e   pl _ te

On the Farm

Name _____

Use the words in the box to fill in the blanks.

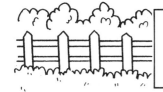

rain	gray	hay	Ray
grain	train	tail	pail

1. The farmer has a _____ horse.

2. He calls the horse _____ .

3. Ray has a black _____ .

4. The horse eats _____ .

5. Ray likes a _____ of oats, too.

6. The farmer grows _____ in the fields.

7. The _____ helps it grow.

8. The _____ takes it to the city.

FS-32502 Big Book of Basic Skills

Feather Words

Name _____

Use the words in the feather to complete the sentences.

feather   thread   bread

read   instead   head

1. Yesterday, I _____ a book about a bird.

2. The bird lost a _____ .

3. A farmer wore it in the hat on his _____ .

4. He fed the bird some _____ crumbs.

5. He gave the bird some _____ to put in its nest.

6. The bird used it _____ of grass.

FS-32502 Big Book of Basic Skills

Riddle Fun

Vowel combinations ea, ee

Name _____

Use the words in the basket to answer the riddles.

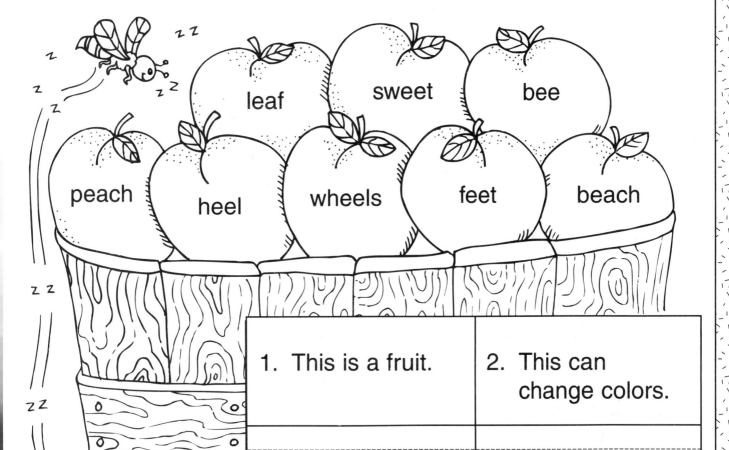

leaf
sweet
bee
peach
heel
wheels
feet
beach

1. This is a fruit.	2. This can change colors.

3. A truck has these.	4. This is on a shoe.	5. You can swim here.
6. This is a taste.	7. This goes buzz.	8. You have two of these.

FS-32502 Big Book of Basic Skills

Boat Ride

Name _____

Use the words on the boat to complete the sentences.

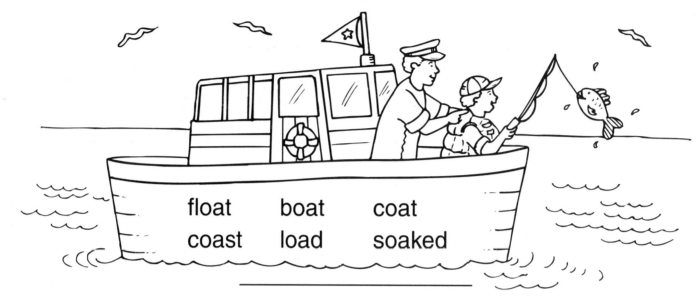

float   boat   coat
coast   load   soaked

1. Would you like a _____ ride?

2. Let's _____ up the boat.

3. Remember to wear a _____ .

4. A life jacket will help you _____ .

5. My hat got _____ .

6. We will sail toward the _____ .

Listen to Y

Name _____

Look at the words and numbers below.
Write the number of each word in the correct box.

1. fry	3. penny	5. fly	7. cry
2. sky	4. bunny	6. baby	8. sunny

Write the words in the correct list.

y as in **funny**	**y** as in **my**
bunny	

FS-32502 Big Book of Basic Skills

Through the Woods

Name _____

Write the vowel sound you hear in each word.
Color the stones.

long vowels = blue   short vowels = brown

Long or Short?

Distinguishing between short
and long vowels

Name _____

Read the words in each box. Decide if each word has a short or a long
vowel. Write the words on the correct pencils.

long vowels	short vowels

cake

hat

feet

pipe

job

soap

nut

sale

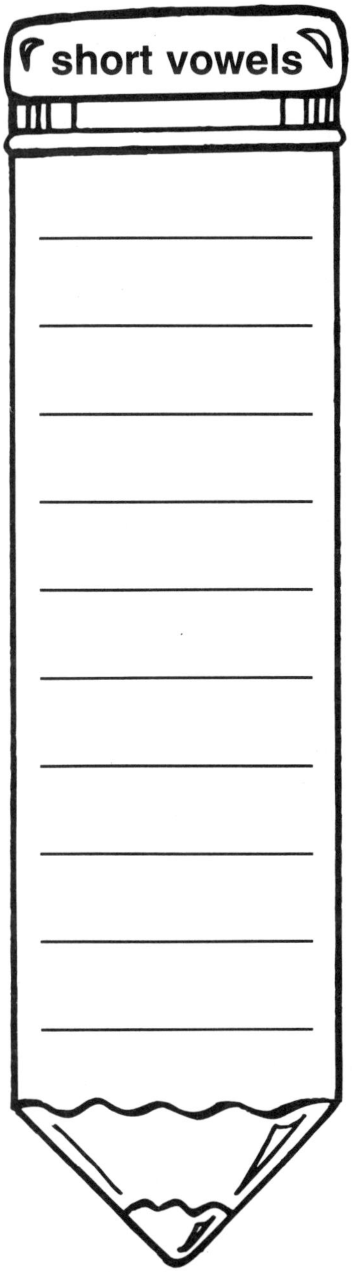

step

pig

up

mop

mule

hill

tap

hope

cube

be

flag

dime

FS-32502 Big Book of Basic Skills

Which One?

Name _____

Circle the words that go with the pictures.
Write each word you circled in the correct list below.

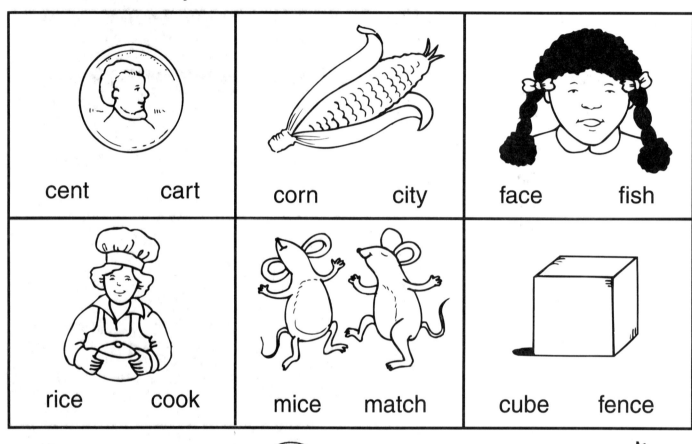

cent　　cart	corn　　city	face　　fish
rice　　cook	mice　　match	cube　　fence

soft c　　　　　　**hard c**

_____　　_____

_____　　_____

_____　　_____

_____　　_____

FS-32502 Big Book of Basic Skills

On Stage

Name _____

Read the story. Color each box.

hard g = | green | soft g = | blue |

Our class will | go | to the | gym | today. We

will see a play about a | giant | . The play will be

on the | stage | . In the play, the | good |

| giant | | grows | | vegetables | in his

| garden | . Then he is surprised when they turn

into shiny | gold | and sparkling | gems | .

FS-32502 Big Book of Basic Skills

What Do You Hear?

Name _____

Listen to the beginning sounds.
Write **sh** or **th** to make the words.

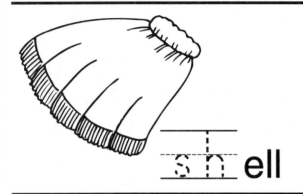 s h ell

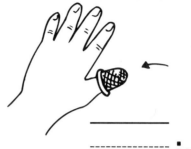 _____ imble

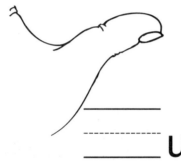 _____ umb

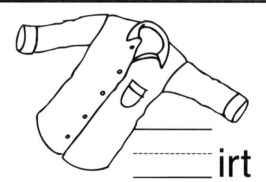 _____ irt

 _____ ip

 _____ oe

 _____ eep

 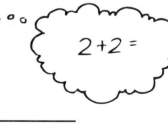 _____ ink

2 + 2 =

52

Places to Go

Name _____

Fill in the correct digraphs. Read the clues.
Draw lines to the right pictures.

sh   **ch**

1.
Catch a fi _____ .

Look for _____ells.

2.
Feed the _____ickens.

See the _____eep.

3.
Go _____opping.

Buy some _____oes.

4.
Pit_____ a tent.

_____ op some wood.

5.
_____ ase a squirrel.

Sit on a ben _____ .

FS-32502 Big Book of Basic Skills

Name That Sound

Name _____

Listen to the beginning sounds.
Write **wh** or **ch** in the boxes.
Circle the word that names each picture.

chin (whale)	wheat chair
chimney white	wheel check
when chick	where chalk
whisper chest	church whiskers

Know Your Blends

Blends with r

Name _____

Color the pictures that begin with the blends.

br		**gr**	
dr	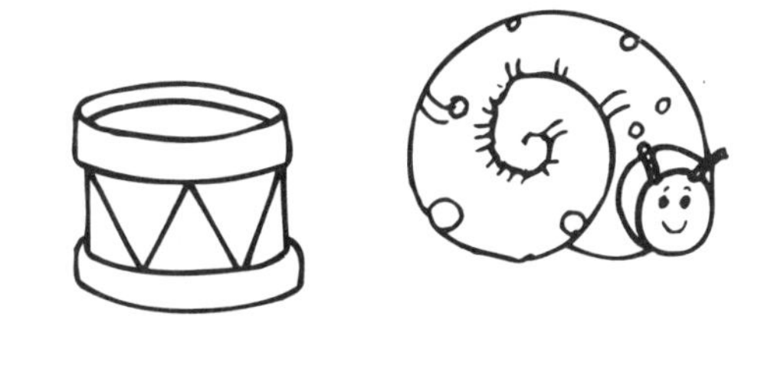	**tr**	
fr		**br**	
dr		**fr**	
tr		**tr**	
cr		**pr**	

57

Where Do I Belong?

Name _____

Look at the words and numbers below.
Write the number of each word in the correct box.

1. clown   3. flag   5. plant   7. slide
2. flower 4. glove   6. glue   8. plug

Choose two words from the list above. Write a sentence for each one.

Schoolroom

Sound of oo (room)

Name _____

Use the words on the chalkboard to answer the riddles.

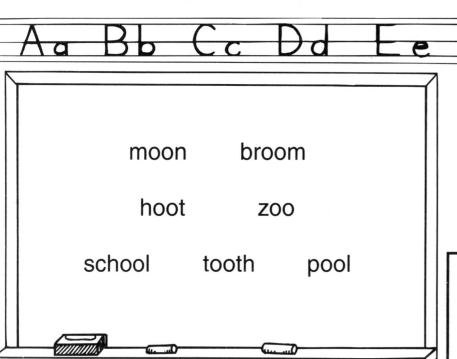

moon   broom

hoot   zoo

school   tooth   pool

CLASS 2B

1. A place to learn

- - - - - - - - - - - - - - -

2. Animals live here.	3. Sweep the floor with this.	4. Go for a swim here.
5. An owl does this.	6. It is in the sky.	7. It is in your mouth.

FS-32502 Big Book of Basic Skills

Look for oo

Name _____

Fill in the vowels **oo**. Read the clues.
Draw lines to the right pictures.

1. This is where to l_____k

   for a b_____k.

2. Drop your fishing h_____k

   into the br_____k.

3. Ben t_____k this

   from the horse's h_____f.

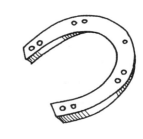

4. This w_____d will

   make a g_____d fire.

5. The c_____k made

   a g_____d meal.

FS-32502 Big Book of Basic Skills

Book or Boot?

Name _____

Read each word below. Decide if the word has the **oo** sound as is **book** or the **oo** sound as in **boot**. Write the words in the correct boxes.

tool

took

moon

school

hook

room

good

foot

tooth

hood

roof

cook

soon

wood

pool

stood

shook

look

mood

zoo

book

_____   _____

_____   _____

_____   _____

_____   _____

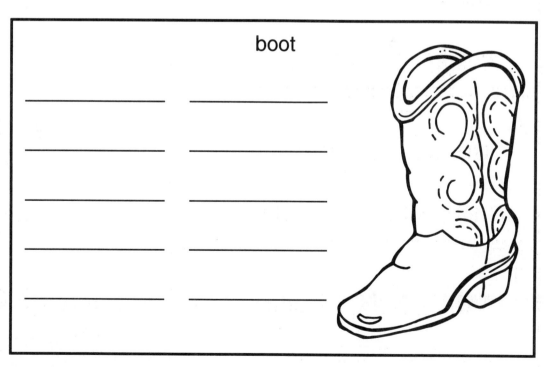

boot

_____   _____

_____   _____

_____   _____

_____   _____

61

Word Art

Name _____

Write the correct word in each sentence.

shark   cart   farm   art

stars   Mark

Mrs. Brown

1. Mrs. Brown teaches _____ classes.

2. She has a _____ for clay, paints, and brushes.

3. One girl made a _____ in deep water.

4. One boy made a sky with _____ .

5. I want to make clay animals on a _____ .

6. My friend _____ will make animals, too.

Finding Words

Diphthongs: oi, oy

Name _____

Read each story.
Circle the words with **oi** and **oy**.
Write the words in the correct lists.

Here is a (boy).

He has a coin.

He wants a toy.

Roy cooks the fish.

He puts on some oil.

He wraps it in foil.

oi

_____

_____

_____

oy

boy

_____

_____

FS-32502 Big Book of Basic Skills

Riddle, Riddle

Name _____

Write the answer to each riddle.

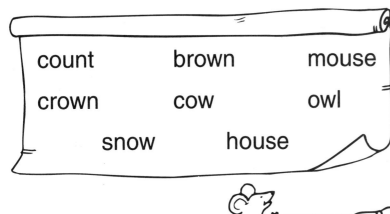

count   brown   mouse

crown   cow   owl

snow   house

1. It can squeak.
_____
_____

2. A king has one.
_____
_____

3. It gives milk.
_____
_____

4. One, two, three.
_____
_____

5. It can fly.
_____
_____

6. It is a color.
_____
_____

7. It is white and wet.
_____
_____

8. People live in it.
_____
_____

FS-32502 Big Book of Basic Skills

Quiet, Please!

Name _____

Color the boxes with silent consonants red.
Color the pictures.

| l | a | m | b |

| w | r | e | a | t | h |

| k | n | i | f | e |

| w | r | i | t | e |

| c | o | m | b |

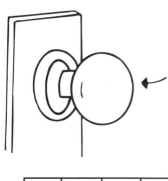

| k | n | o | b |

| k | n | i | t |

| l | i | m | b |

| t | h | u | m | b |

FS-32502 Big Book of Basic Skills

Think!

Name _____

Circle the word for each picture. Color the pictures.

string stick	ham hang	ride ring
soft sink	stamp sting	skunk skip
wing whip	swing sweet	stop strong
jump junk	sell sing	trunk track

Double consonants
with -ing

Batter Up

Name _____

Match.

run   winning

clap   running

bat   batting

win   clapping

1. Sara picks up the _____.

2. She is good at _____ the ball.

3. Sara makes a home _____.

4. The fans are _____.

5. Our team is _____.

Introduction

CHAPTER 3

Grammar

Reading and writing are the cornerstones of education. The basics of these skills include reading comprehension and a working knowledge of grammar and spelling. Language class, in which students develop their foundation of English, should be an enjoyable, educational experience for all students. This is possible, however, only if students are conscious of steady progress in their written language, and if they understand what they are doing.

This chapter has been designed to help students succeed in grammar usage. The activities were created to help students feel confident about their grammar skills and help them understand the steps involved in learning these skills.

The pages have been arranged in an easy-to-follow format. This format allows the teacher to choose from a variety of second-grade grammar skills that are presented in an interesting, relevant, and age-appropriate manner. Each skill begins with rules. These skills are followed by intensive practice with interesting information. The skills included are those that every second-grade student should possess in order to express himself or herself confidently in spoken and written English.

With more emphasis being placed on the traditional basic subjects, it is easy to understand the vital role grammar plays in everyone's life. It has become clear how important the teaching of grammar is in helping students to become confident in their English usage.

The activities in this chapter can be used alone or as an integral part of any language program. They can also be used in conjunction with literature-based programs to provide students with the benefits of a well-rounded English language education.

Bears, Bears, Bears

Name _____

A **sentence** is a group of words that tells what someone or something is or does. Underline the words below that are not sentences. Add words to make them sentences.

Bears are big animals. Thick fur. They have small eyes and small ears. Bears walk on their four large feet.

Bears eat meat and many other foods. They hunt mice and squirrels. They eat berries, acorns, and nuts. Bears also.

Mother bears have between one and four cubs. Usually have twins. Bear cubs stay in the den for about two months.

There are many kinds of bears. Brown bears largest. Polar bears are also very large. They live in the Arctic. Sun bears are small.

Try This! Write a sentence that tells about the colors of bears.

Skating Fun

Name _____

Write the words below
in the correct order to
make sentences.

1. best My friend Denise. is

_____

2. very is a She good ice skater.

_____

3. Denise turns. can   fancy do

_____

4. teaching to me She is how   skate.

_____

5. ice. I on the Sometimes fall hard

_____

6. like I to backwards. skate

_____

7. skating We fun have together.

_____

Try This! What clues helped you put the sentences in the correct order?

〈70〉

Places to Go

Subject

Name _____

The **subject** part of a sentence tells whom or what the sentence is about.
Read each sentence. Write a subject for it.

1. _____

_____ went

to the art museum.

2. _____

_____

is my favorite artist.

3. _____

_____ would like

hiking in the forest.

4. _____

_____ live

in the forest.

5. _____

_____ is

a good swimmer.

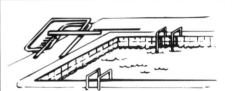

6. _____

_____ is

where I like to swim.

7. _____

_____ are planning

a vacation.

8. _____

_____ is

where I want to go.

9. _____

is a good place to

go to on a rainy day.

Try This! Write a sentence that has a friend of yours as the subject.

71

What's Happening?

Name _____

The **predicate** part of a sentence tells what the subject does or is.

Write a predicate to finish each sentence.

1. My friend and I _____

_____

2. A scary-looking spider _____

_____

3. Three tiny ladybugs _____

4. My family _____

5. The blue whale _____

6. Valentine's Day _____

7. Snowflakes _____

8. That calculator _____

9. Our favorite playground _____

_____

10. My very best friend _____

_____

_____

Try This!

Write a sentence telling your favorite thing to do. Underline the predicate.

FS-32502 Big Book of Basic Skills

Pretty Strange Pets

Name _____

A sentence has two main parts:

1. The **subject** tells whom or what the sentence is about.
2. The **predicate** tells what is happening.

Read the subjects and predicates below. Mix and match them to make four silly sentences. Write them below.

Subjects
Mary's boa
Grandma's fish
That spotted pony
The gerbil family
My new puppy
Todd's rabbit
Their parrot

Predicates
sings "Happy Birthday."
can do a back flip.
goes to school.
plays the piano.
does the dishes for me.
watches too much TV.
is learning to ride a bike.

1. _____

_____

2. _____

_____

3. _____

_____

4. _____

_____

_____

Try This!   Write another predicate to add to the box.

73   FS-32502 Big Book of Basic Skills

Flower Fun

Name _____

A **telling sentence** tells you something. It begins with a capital letter and ends with a period (**.**).

Color this picture. Use it to write four telling sentences.

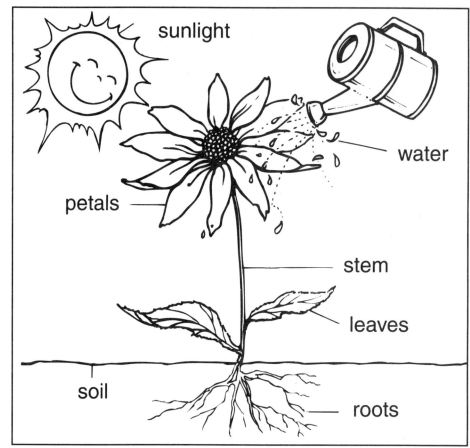

Example

A flower is a plant.

1. _____

    _____

2. _____

    _____

3. _____

    _____

4. _____

    _____

 Write a telling sentence about a flower you like.

⟨74⟩

A Talking Tiger

Name _____

An **asking sentence** asks a question.
It begins with a capital letter and ends
with a question mark (**?**).

Pretend you have met a talking tiger.
Write five questions you would like to
ask it.

Example

How did you learn to talk?

1. _____

_____

2. _____

_____

3. _____

_____

4. _____

_____

5. _____

_____

Try This!   Write a question the tiger might ask you.

FS-32502 Big Book of Basic Skills

Annie Jump Cannon

Name _____

Read each sentence.

If it is a telling sentence, write **T** and the missing period.

If it is an asking sentence, write **A** and the missing question mark.

A 1. Do you know who Annie Jump Cannon was _?_

T 2. She lived about 100 years ago _._

___ 3. Annie Jump Cannon was an astronomer __

___ 4. Do you know what that is __

___ 5. An astronomer is a scientist who studies the sky __

___ 6. Annie loved to watch the stars when she was little __

___ 7. She would sit up on the roof of her house __

___ 8. Do you ever watch the stars at night __

___ 9. Can you find the Big Dipper in the sky __

___ 10. Annie went to college to learn more about space __

___ 11. She would study the sky by looking through a telescope __

___ 12. Have you ever used a telescope __

___ 13. Annie Jump Cannon became an important astronomer __

___ 14. She created a way of grouping stars by the light they make __

Try This! Write a sentence telling what you want to be when you grow up.

FS-32502 Big Book of Basic Skills

Wow!

Name _____

An **exclamation** is a sentence that shows strong feeling.
It begins with a capital letter and ends with an exclamation point (**!**).
Read each setting. Write an exclamation you might say.

1. Your story won first prize.

_____

2. You spilled paint all over.

_____

3. Your dog wet your bed.

_____

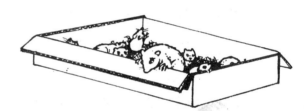

4. Your hamster had its babies.

_____

5. You broke a window.

_____

6. Your friend gets to sleep over.

_____

Try This! Read aloud your exclamations using expression in your voice.

FS-32502 Big Book of Basic Skills

Dandy Dinos

Delarative, interrogative, and exclamatory sentences

Name _____

Read what the children below said on their field trip.
Write the missing period (.) at the end of a telling sentence.
Write the missing question mark (?) at the end of an asking sentence.
Write the missing exclamation point (!) at the end of an exclamation.

Wow, look how big it is

How do they know dinosaurs didn't drag their tails

Machines make these dinosaur models move

Which was the biggest dinosaur

That dinosaur is going to get you. Watch out

Paleontologists are scientists who study dinosaurs

Could we go on a dinosaur dig

This is a claw of a tyrannosaurus

What did stegosaurus use its plates for

Thank you

Try This! Write a telling sentence, a question, and an exclamation you might say at a dinosaur museum.

78

Mixed-Up Commands

Name _____

A **command** is a sentence that tells someone to do something. It begins with a capital letter and ends with a period.

Jason and Sam created a robot. They are giving their friend Joe commands to see if it works. Unscramble the words below to create the commands.

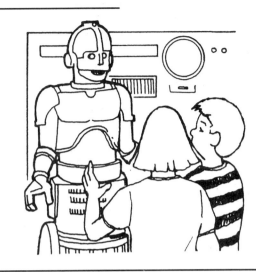

1. office Go our to

_____

2. the Open door red

_____

3. shortest the Find robot

_____

4. blue its knob for Look

_____

5. knob the three Turn times

_____

6. to robot Tell the us to come

_____

Try This! Write a command you would give the robot.

〈79〉 FS-32502 Big Book of Basic Skills

Nouns at the Beach

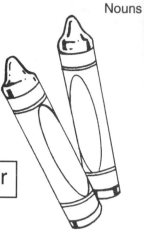

Name _____

A **noun** names a person, place, or thing.

Find the nouns listed below in the picture. Color them.

| birds | sailboats | clouds | girls | umbrellas | Snack Bar |

Then write four more nouns you see.

_____   _____

_____   _____

Try This!   Make a list of nouns you can touch from where you are sitting.

Busy Butterflies

Name _____

A **proper noun** names a special person, place, or thing. It begins with a capital letter.

Read the nouns on the butterfly wings. Color the wings that have proper nouns.

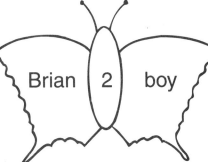

girl 1 Teresa

Brian 2 boy

cat 3 Fluffy

book 4 *Crow Boy*

day 5 Friday

May 6 month

Texas 7 state

New York City 8 city

Saturn 9 planet

principal 10 Mrs. Stone

 **Try This!** Write a proper noun to match each of these words: *school, friend, pet.*

FS-32502 Big Book of Basic Skills

Find, Count, and Write

Name _____

A **plural noun** names more than one person, place, or thing.
Most end with the letter **s**.

Find, count, and write the nouns below. Add an **s** to make them plural.

A.
chair _5 chairs_____

B.
desk _____

C.
rabbit _____

D.
book _____

E.
globe _____

F.
crayon _____

G.
pencil _____

H.
computer _____

I.
clock _____

J.
plant _____

Try This! Write a sentence telling how many chairs are in your room.

Match Them Up

Name _____

A **plural noun** names more than one person, place, or thing. Most nouns are made plural by adding the letter **s**. But the nouns on this page are different.

Draw lines to match each noun to its plural.

One	More Than One	One	More Than One
fox	boxes	party	babies
ax	foxes	city	leaves
box	buses	baby	parties
bus	axes	leaf	cities
dress	lunches	wolf	elves
kiss	dresses	elf	wolves
lunch	kisses	child	women
peach	inches	man	moose
inch	bushes	woman	men
bush	ashes	moose	children
wish	peaches	deer	sheep
ash	wishes	sheep	deer

Try This! If a word ends in *x, s, ch,* or *sh,* how do you make it plural?

FS-32502 Big Book of Basic Skills

A Heat Experiment

Name _____

bowls	minute
cubes	seconds
heat	spoon
friends	spoons

Proofread the story below. Find and underline the nouns that are wrong. Write each one correctly on the line. Use the words from the bowl.

1. _____   Yesterday my three friend and I did a science

2. _____   experiment. We wanted to find out if heats travels

through some things better than others.

3. _____   First we found three spoons. One spoons was

metal, one was plastic, and one was wooden. Then

4. _____   we got two bowl. We filled one with cold water and

5. _____   lots of ice cube. My mom filled the other one with

hot water.

6. _____   We put all the spoon in the bowl of hot water.

7. _____   Then we waited for thirty second. We felt the spoons

to see if they were warm. The metal spoon was the

warmest. Next, we put all the spoons in the bowl of

8. _____   ice water. This time we waited for one minutes.

Which spoon do you think was the coldest?

Try This!   Write how you knew one of the nouns was wrong.

Verbs at the Circus

Name _____

A **verb** is an action word.

Find the pictures that match the verbs below. Color them.

| swings | balance | drinking | step | bow | follows |

Then write four more verbs that match the picture.

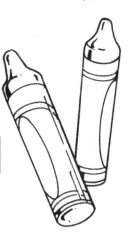

_____   _____

_____   _____

Try This! Write a sentence that tells what you would like to do at a
circus. Underline the verb.

A Penguin Puppet

Name _____

Am, is, and *are* are special verbs.
They are not action words.
They tell about someone or something.

Use **is** with one person, place, or thing.
Use **are** with more than one or with the word *you.*
Use **am** with the word *I.*

Mike is making his penguin puppet speak.
Fill in the correct verb—**am, is,** or **are**—in each sentence below.

1. I _____ a penguin.

2. My name _____ Waddles.

3. I _____ from Antarctica.

4. Antarctica _____ south of here.

5. My friends _____ still there.

6. We _____ good swimmers and divers.

7. _____ you a good swimmer?

8. Penguins _____ birds.

9. But a penguin _____ not a flying bird.

10. I _____ a waddling bird.

Try This! Draw a picture of yourself holding a puppet. Write a caption showing what the puppet is saying. Use one of the following verbs: *am, is, are.*

FS-32502 Big Book of Basic Skills

All About Raccoons

Subject/Verb agreement

Name _____

Fill in the blanks below with one of the verbs written on the log.

1.	2.	3.	4.	5.	6.	7.	8.
is	lives	makes	hunts	eats	uses	sleeps	has
are	live	make	hunt	eat	use	sleep	have

1. A raccoon _____ a mammal.

2. Some raccoons _____ in forests.

3. They _____ their den in a hollow log or a tree.

4. Raccoons _____ at night.

5. They _____ fish, frogs, nuts, fruit, eggs, and seeds.

6. A raccoon _____ its strong claws for climbing.

7. In cold places, raccoons _____ a lot in winter.

8. Baby raccoons do not _____ rings on their tails when they are born.

Try This! Write a question you have about raccoons. Circle the verb.

FS-32502 Big Book of Basic Skills

A Past Tense Puzzle

Name _____

Some verbs tell what happened in the past. They often end in **ed**.

Read the verbs. In the puzzle, write the past tense of the verbs.

Across
1. trick
5. sail
7. spell
9. want
12. look
13. need

Down
2. end
3. ask
4. miss
6. plant
8. add
9. work
10. learn
11. help

Try This! Write three more past tense verbs that end with *ed*.

88

Past Tense Match-up

Irregular past tense verbs

Name _____

Not all verbs that show past time end in **ed**.
Draw lines to match up the present tense
and past tense verbs.

Today I ...	Yesterday I ...
write •	• thought
read •	• wrote
think •	• said
say •	• read

Today I ...	Yesterday I ...
go •	• flew
run •	• ran
fly •	• went
swim •	• stood
ride •	• swam
stand •	• rode

Today I ...	Yesterday I ...
eat •	• saw
drink •	• heard
see •	• ate
hear •	• drank
have •	• lost
lose •	• had

Today I ...	Yesterday I ...
give •	• took
take •	• made
make •	• left
get •	• gave
leave •	• came
come •	• got

Try This! Write three sentences using verbs from this page.

FS-32502 Big Book of Basic Skills

Leaved or Left?

Name _____

Have you read any of Barbara Park's books about Junie B. Jones? Junie B. is a funny kindergartner who uses the wrong words a lot when she is speaking.

Read the sentences below. They are what Junie B. sounds like when she is telling about a great day. Circle the past tense verbs that are wrong. Choose the correct verbs from the bus. Write them on the lines.

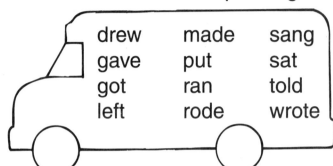

drew	made	sang
gave	put	sat
got	ran	told
left	rode	wrote

_____ 1. I leaved my house.

_____ 2. I rided the bus to school.

_____ 3. I getted off the bus like a lady.

_____ 4. I runned to my class.

_____ 5. I singed "America the Beautiful."

_____ 6. I maked a picture.

_____ 7. I drawed it really good.

_____ 8. I writed my name neatly.

_____ 9. I gived it to my teacher.

_____ 10. She putted a star on it.

_____ 11. I telled Jim that my picture was the best.

_____ 12. I sitted down and smiled.

Junie B.

Try This! Write a sentence telling about a book you read that you liked.

FS-32502 Big Book of Basic Skills

Wacky Wibbles

Name _____

An **adjective** is a word that describes a person, place, or thing.

Find Wibbles in the picture that match the adjectives below. Color them.

tall	round	bumpy	happy	sad	young

Then write four more adjectives that match the picture.

_____   _____

_____   _____

Try This! Draw a Wibble that is blue, short, silly, and square.

An Adjective Game

Name _____

Play the game below with a partner. You will need a coin. Listen for directions.

An **adjective** is a word that tells about a person, place, or thing.

Smart, happy, big, red, cold, metal, and round are all adjectives.

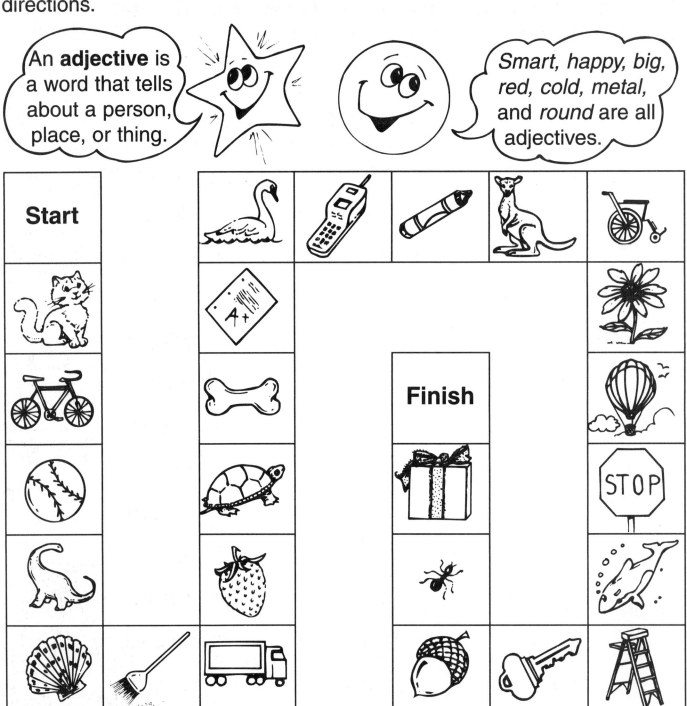

Teacher: Give students the following directions: 1. Cut out a square from scrap paper and color it to make your game piece. 2. Taking turns, flip a coin to move. 3. If it's heads, move ahead two spaces and name two adjectives that describe the picture you landed on. If it's tails, move ahead three spaces and name three adjectives that describe the picture you landed on. 4. If you both agree your adjectives are correct, you can stay on that space, and your turn is over. If you agree your adjectives are wrong, move back one space, and your turn is over. 5. The first player to reach Finish wins.

92   FS-32502 Big Book of Basic Skills

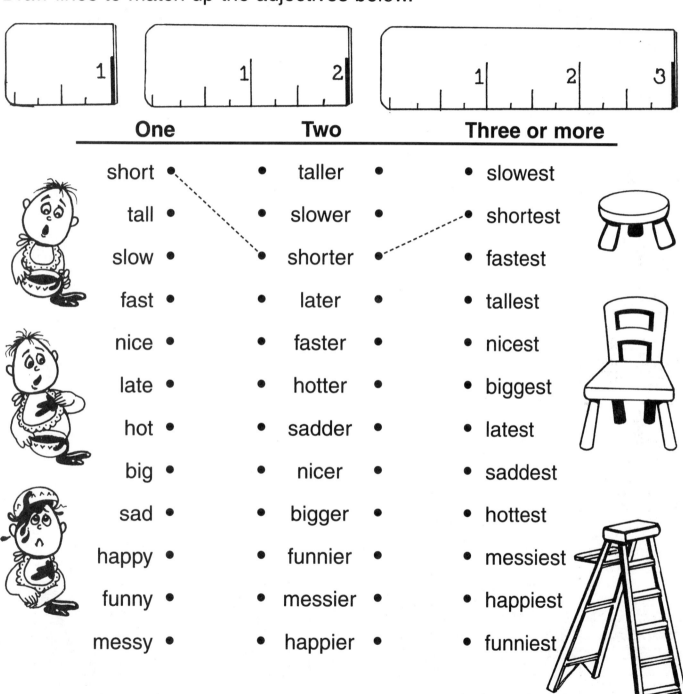

Short, Shorter, Shortest

Comparative and superlative adjectives

Name _____

Adjectives that compare two things often end in **er**.
Adjectives that compare three or more things often end in **est**.
Draw lines to match up the adjectives below.

One	Two	Three or more
short	taller	slowest
tall	slower	shortest
slow	shorter	fastest
fast	later	tallest
nice	faster	nicest
late	hotter	biggest
hot	sadder	latest
big	nicer	saddest
sad	bigger	hottest
happy	funnier	messiest
funny	messier	happiest
messy	happier	funniest

Try This!

Choose a set of adjectives such as *happy, happier,* and *happiest.* Draw and label three pictures to match.

93

FS-32502 Big Book of Basic Skills

Bugs, Bugs, Bugs

Name _____

A and *an* are special adjectives called **articles**.

- Use **an** if the next word starts with a vowel sound.
- Use **a** if the next word starts with a consonant sound.

Example *an* insect   *a* bug

Bobby made a list of insects he has seen in books. Complete the list below by adding **a** or **an** before each insect.

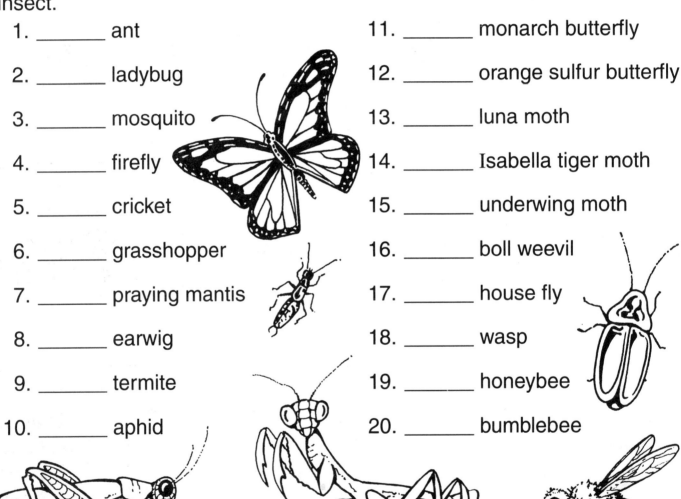

1. _____ ant
2. _____ ladybug
3. _____ mosquito
4. _____ firefly
5. _____ cricket
6. _____ grasshopper
7. _____ praying mantis
8. _____ earwig
9. _____ termite
10. _____ aphid

11. _____ monarch butterfly
12. _____ orange sulfur butterfly
13. _____ luna moth
14. _____ Isabella tiger moth
15. _____ underwing moth
16. _____ boll weevil
17. _____ house fly
18. _____ wasp
19. _____ honeybee
20. _____ bumblebee

Try This! Write a sentence about an insect you have seen. Use **a** or **an** in your sentence.

94

Pronoun Pictures

Name _____

A **noun** names a person, place, or thing.
A **pronoun** is a word that can take the place of a noun.
I, you, he, she, it, we, and *they* are all pronouns.

Look at each picture.
Write the matching pronoun from the pencil.

I
he
she
it
we
they

1. _____

2. _____

3. _____

4. _____

5. _____

6. _____

7. _____

8. _____

Draw
yourself
here.

$\rightarrow$

9. _____

Draw a
friend and
yourself
here.

$\leftarrow$

10. _____

Try This!

Choose three pronouns. Write each one in a sentence.

FS-32502 Big Book of Basic Skills

A Costume Party

Name _____

The **pronouns** *you, me, him, her, it, us,* and *them*
take the place of a person, place, or thing.
They follow action words or words like *to, of,* and *for.*

her   it
him   us
me   them

Fill in each blank with a pronoun from the balloon
that takes the place of the underlined words.

1. <u>My family and I</u> went to a big party at my Aunt Marsha's house.

   She told _____ to wear our costumes.

2. My cousin Jonah's <u>costume</u> was a giant tooth.

   He made _____ out of cardboard.

3. Jonah's friends <u>Annie and Kim</u> came as a horse.

   Aunt Marsha gave _____ an award for best team costume.

4. <u>I</u> came as a frog.

   My parents took a picture of _____.

5. My friend <u>Dave</u> was a dinosaur.

   I helped _____ carry his tail.

6. <u>Aunt Marsha</u> was a cactus.

   I asked _____ if she got tired holding up her arms.

Try This! Write a sentence that has the pronoun **you** after one of the
following words: *to, for, with.*

〈 96 〉 FS-32502 Big Book of Basic Skills

Meet Mousie

Name _____

An **adverb** describes an action.
Most adverbs end in **ly.**

Choose an adverb from the box
to answer each question.

Adverb Box		
quickly	quietly	neatly
slowly	loudly	sloppily
carefully	happily	badly
proudly	sadly	well

1. How does Mousie run?

_____

2. How does Mousie sing?

_____

3. How does Mousie write?

_____

4. How does Mousie draw?

_____

5. How does Mousie play?

_____

6. How does Mousie work?

_____

7. How does Mousie march?

_____

8. How does Mousie read?

_____

9. How does Mousie ride?

_____

Try This! Write a sentence about yourself using one of the adverbs.

FS-32502 Big Book of Basic Skills

Introduction

CHAPTER 4

Mechanics

Reading and writing are the cornerstones of education. The basics of these skills include reading comprehension and a working knowledge of the mechanics, or capitalization and punctuation, of language. Language class, in which students develop their foundation of English, should be an enjoyable, educational experience for all students. This is possible, however, only if students are conscious of steady progress in their written language, and if they understand what they are doing.

The activities in this chapter have been designed to help students succeed in the language mechanics skills involving capitalization and punctuation. The activities were created to help students learn, practice, and feel confident about these language mechanics skills and to help them understand the steps involved in learning these skills.

The pages have been arranged in an easy-to-follow format. This format allows you to choose from a variety of second-grade language mechanics skills that are presented in an interesting, relevant, and age-appropriate manner. Each skill begins with rules and examples. These are followed by intensive practice by means of interesting information. At the end of the chapter are review pages students can complete to see how well they have understood the skills presented. The skills included are those that every second-grade student should possess in order to express himself or herself confidently in written English.

Today, more emphasis is being placed on the traditional basic subjects. This is because these subjects, including the mechanics of English, play a vital role in a student's ability to understand the world and to become a competent and articulate player in it. Teaching language mechanics is essential in preparing students to become confident in their English usage.

The activities in this chapter can be used alone or as an integral part of any language program. It can also be used in conjunction with literature-based programs to provide students with the benefits of a well-rounded English language education.

Pretty Neat Pets

Capitalization—
Proper names

Name _____

All names, even names of pets, begin with capital letters.

Examples *Janie*   *Muffin, my cat*

Each student brought a pet to school for Pet Sharing Day. It was amazing!
Every pet had the same beginning letter in its name as its owner.

Example *Bruce's pet is Barney.*

Match each student to his or her pet.

Student	**Pet**
1. Lucy	Marty—hamster
2. Susie	Fluffy—cat
3. Henry	Pumpkin—chow dog
4. Felicia	Hairy—guinea pig
5. Merrill	Goldie—goldfish
6. Angela	Lovey—bird
7. Peter	Sassie—big dog
8. Gordon	Angel—cat

Write whose pet is whose.

9. Lucy's pet is _____.   13. Merrill's pet is _____.

10. Susie's pet is _____.   14. Angela's pet is _____.

11. Henry's pet is _____.   15. Peter's pet is _____.

12. Felicia's pet is _____.   16. Gordon's pet is _____.

Try This!   Write seven pet names that begin with the first letter of your
name.

FS-32502 Big Book of Basic Skills

Special Places

Name _____

The names of important places begin with capital letters.

Examples *Jacksonville Zoo   Mount Everest*

Use the places listed below to tell where the children like to go. Hint: Each child likes to go to a place that begins with the same letter as his or her name.

- Oceans of Fun
- Disneyland
- Adventure Landing
- Super City Science Museum
- Harrisonville History Museum
- Barnett Baseball Park

1. David likes to go to _____.

2. Ollie likes to go to _____.

3. Bob likes to go to _____.

4. Adam likes to go to _____.

5. Halie likes to go to _____.

6. Sue likes to go to _____.

Capitalize any important places below that need to be capitalized. Write them on the lines. Hint: Three places do not need to be capitalized.

waterworld	Pete's petting park	Jerry's ice cream parlor
baseball field	grocery store	david's department store
columbia zoo	mount rushmore	amusement park

7. _____   10. _____

8. _____   11. _____

9. _____   12. _____

Try This! Write the name of a special place you like to go to that begins with the first letter in your name.

〈100〉

Scary Sharks

Name _____

Every sentence begins with a capital letter.

Examples   *Many people are scared of sharks.*
Some sharks are very big.

Read the story below. Circle each letter
that should be a capital letter.
Write the words correctly on the lines.

1. _____

2. _____

3. _____

4. _____

5. _____

6. _____

7. _____

8. _____

9. _____

10. _____

11. _____

12. _____

13. _____

14. _____

sharks are a kind of fish. there are about
300 kinds of sharks. they live in oceans all
over the world.

some sharks get as big as 60 feet long. they
can even weigh two times as much as an
elephant. other sharks are small. the
smallest sharks are only four inches long.

sharks are different from other kinds of fish.
they do not have bones like other fish. some
sharks even eat their own babies!

be careful when you swim in the ocean.
sharks have a great sense of smell. they
have good hearing, too. if a human is
swimming 1,000 yards away, a shark can
hear it.

Try This! Write three facts about another animal that lives in the ocean.
Use capital letters when needed.

FS-32502 Big Book of Basic Skills

Don't Be Me First!

Name _____

The word **I** is always written as a capital letter.

Examples   *I am hungry*
                Mom said I can go.

Write the sentences below correctly.
Capitalize any lowercase i's where necessary.

1. i went to the dentist.

   _____

2. Jan and i ride our bikes to school.

   _____

3. i like to read funny books.

   _____

4. My mom said i can go swimming.

   _____

5. i love pizza.

   _____

6. Can i come too?

   _____

7. Will i get a treat today?

   _____

Write three sentences using *I*.

8. _____

9. _____

10. _____

Try This!   Write two sentences using the word *I*.

〈102〉 FS-32502 Big Book of Basic Skills

Please Stay in Order

Name _____

The days of the week always follow the same order. The days of the week always start with capital letters.

Sunday	Monday	Tuesday	Wednesday	Thursday	Friday	Saturday

1. The first day of the week is _____.

2. The first day of the school week is _____.

3. The last day of the week is _____.

4. The last day of the school week is _____.

5. The two weekend days are _____ and _____.

6. The middle day of the week is _____.

7. The two days that begin with *T* are _____ and _____.

8. The two days that begin with *S* are _____ and _____.

9. What is your favorite day of the week? _____

   Why? _____

   _____

10. Write the days of the school week in order. _____

    _____

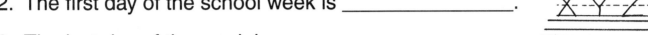
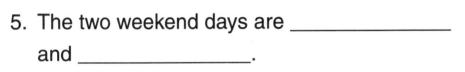
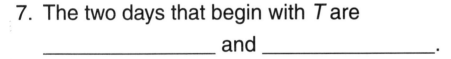
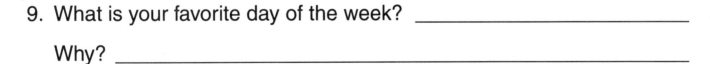

Try This! Draw a picture of you doing something on your favorite day of the week. Label what day it is.

Oops! Out of Order!

Name _____

The months of the year start with capital letters.

Examples   *January*   *June*

Write the names of the months in the correct order below. (Hint: They should not be in ABC order.)

1. First _____

2. Second _____

3. Third _____

4. Fourth _____

5. Fifth _____

6. Sixth _____

7. Seventh _____

8. Eighth _____

9. Ninth _____

10. Tenth _____

11. Eleventh _____

12. Twelfth _____

Memorize this poem:

30 days hath September, April, June, and November.
All the rest have 31—except February.

List the months below that have . . .

30 days

1. _____

2. _____

3. _____

4. _____

28 days

1. _____

31 days

1. _____

2. _____

3. _____

4. _____

5. _____

6. _____

7. _____

Try This!   Write what your favorite month is and why.

Let's Celebrate!

Name _____

Names of holidays begin with capital letters.

Examples *Valentine's **D**ay*   *Labor **D**ay*

Dates begin with capital letters.

Examples *January 1*   *November 10*

Write a sentence for each holiday and date below. Use capital letters where needed.

Example *valentine's day/february 14 → Valentine's Day is February 14.*

1. labor day/september

   _____

2. mother's day/may

   _____

3. father's day/june

   _____

4. st. patrick's day/march 17

   _____

5. thanksgiving day/november

   _____

6. martin luther king, jr.'s birthday/january

   _____

7. independence day/july 4

   _____

8. new year's day/january 1

   _____

Try This! Write a story about your favorite holiday.

Letter Fun

Name _____

An initial is the first letter of a name or a word. It is written as a capital letter and followed by a period.

Example *Mary Ann Duncan → M.A.D.*

Read the list of names below. Write the initials.

1. Lindsay Ruth Turnbach _____

2. Samantha Rachel Farley_____

3. Mary Kate Kane _____

4. Todd Michael Rowe_____

5. Charles Walker Shepherd _____

6. Timmy Lee Jones _____

7. Michelle Jean Berry _____

8. Tyler James Monroe _____

Write names for the initials below.

9. T.J.K.

_____

10. M.M.M.

_____

11. K.T.C.

_____

12. L.A.T.

_____

13. N.A.D.

_____

14. S.R.Z.

_____

Try This! Write your initials and the initials of every member of your family.

FS-32502 Big Book of Basic Skills

Sending a Letter

Name _____

The greeting of a letter begins with a capital letter.

Examples *Dear Tom,* *Dearest Emily,*

Finish the greetings below. Use *Dear, To,* or *Dearest.*

1. _____ Mom,

2. _____ Aunt Janie,

3. _____ Bobby,

4. _____ Mary Sue,

5. _____ Laurie,

6. _____ Grandpa,

The first word in the closing of a letter begins with a capital letter.

Examples *Love,* *Your friend,*

In a letter, the name of the person sending the letter goes under the closing.

Write a closing on each line below. Choose from some of these closings: *Love, Your friend, Yours truly, As always.*

7. _____,
   Dad

8. _____,
   Grandma

9. _____,
   Maggie

10. _____,
    Keith

11. _____,
    Penny

12. _____,
    Sam

Try This! Write a short letter to a friend.

Thank-you Note

Name _____

In a friendly letter, these words begin with capital letters:

- the first word in the greeting   *Dear Jimmy,*
- the first word in the closing   *Love,*
- the first word of each sentence
- special names of people, places, and things
- the word *I*
- dates

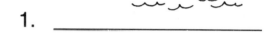

Some capital letters are missing in the letter below. Write the words that need capital letters on the lines.

june 1, 1997

dear Grandma,

thank you for the beach ball. we went to the beach, and i played with it all day. the wind came along and blew it away. i had to chase it forever. chuck, the lifeguard, saw it rolling. he told me where it went. there it was behind the sand dune.

love,

jessica

1. _____
2. _____
3. _____
4. _____
5. _____
6. _____
7. _____
8. _____
9. _____
10. _____
11. _____
12. _____

Try This!   Write a thank-you note to someone.

FS-32502 Big Book of Basic Skills

State Names

Capitalization—State and
city names

Name _____

State names begin with capital letters.

Examples *California   Tennessee*

Uh oh! Chandler visited a lot of states but
he forgot to capitalize them in his report.
Help him out. Write the name of each
state correctly on the lines.

One summer, my parents took me out
west. We visited Disneyland in california.
Then we saw beautiful mountains in
oregon. After oregon, we went to
washington. The Grand Coulee Dam is so
big! montana was next. There we went to
Glacier National Park. What big mountains
we saw! Finally, we came back to
missouri. We had a great time!

_____   _____   _____

_____   _____   _____

City names also begin with capital letters.

Examples *Des Moines   Austin*

Write the names of 10 cities you know. Use a map to help you.

1. _____   6. _____

2. _____   7. _____

3. _____   8. _____

4. _____   9. _____

5. _____   10. _____

Try This!   Write the name of your state. Write five more states you
would like to visit.

〈109〉   FS-32502 Big Book of Basic Skills

Envelope Etiquette

Name _____

The names of people, streets, cities, and states begin with capital letters.

Examples

Jolene Moore
91577 Oak Street
St. Paul, Minnesota
55101

Robert Estes
124 Hart Street
Tampa, Florida
33601

There are four lines in an address. Fill in your address on the lines below.

1. Name _____

2. Street _____

3. State _____

4. ZIP Code _____

Make up new addresses. Choose one from each list below. Use each one only once.

Name	Street	City, State	ZIP Code
Erica Long	5404 Western Ln.	Toledo, Ohio	43601
Anthony Pugh	125 9th St.	Miami, Florida	33010
Maria Lopez	4927 Hill Ave.	Reno, Nevada	89501

1. _____
2. _____
3. _____
4. _____

1. _____
2. _____
3. _____
4. _____

1. _____
2. _____
3. _____
4. _____

Try This!   Practice writing your complete address.

FS-32502 Big Book of Basic Skills

Give It a Title

Name _____

The first word, last word, and each important word in a title begin with capital letters. Words that have four or more letters begin with capital letters.

Examples *The **B**est **T**rip **I** **E**ver **T**ook**   A **G**iraffe and the **F**ood **I**t **L**ikes*

Write a story title for the descriptions below.

1. This story is about a dog that gets lost. He travels 100 miles before he finds his way home.

   _____

2. This story is about a little boy who gets to meet his favorite professional athlete.

   _____

3. This story is about a girl who scores 10 home runs in one softball game.

   _____

4. This story is about a family that wins $10 million in the lottery.

   _____

5. This story is about a little girl who moves to the U.S.A. from France. Her name is Valerie. She is very scared and shy.

   _____

6. This story is about a monkey that escapes from the zoo and a little boy that becomes his friend.

   _____

7. This story is about a boy who jumped into a computer screen and disappeared.

   _____

8. This story is about two girls who create a robot that will do their homework for them.

   _____

Try This!   Write a story for one of the titles you wrote above.

Favorite Fairy Tales

Name _____

The first word in a book title begins with a capital letter. Every other important word begins with a capital letter. Also, words with four or more letters are capitalized.

Examples *The Beautiful Princess*   *The Dog in the Woods*

Write each book title correctly under the picture it matches.

goldilocks and the three bears   cinderella   sleeping beauty
little red riding hood   the wizard of oz   the gingerbread boy

1. _____

2. _____

3. _____

4. _____

5. _____

6. _____

7. Write the name of your favorite book.

_____

8. Write the name of a book you have right now.

_____

9. Write the name of a funny book you have read.

_____

10. Make up the title of a book you would like to write.

_____

Try This!   Draw your favorite fairy tale character and write the name of the story under it.

Capitalization—Poems

It's Raining!

Name _____

Each important word in the title of a poem begins with a capital letter.

 *Rain, Rain, Go Away*

The first word in every line of a poem begins with a capital letter.

 Rain, rain, go away,
Come again another day.

Read the poem below. Then copy it on the lines provided. Put in capital letters where they belong. Don't forget the title!

> it's raining
> it's raining,
> it's pouring,
> the old man is snoring.
> he went to bed.
> he bumped his head,
> and he couldn't get up
> in the morning.

_____

_____

_____

_____

_____

_____

_____

 **Write another verse to this poem.**

A Good Man

Name _____

Every sentence ends with a special punctuation mark.

A period (.) is used at the end of a telling sentence.

A question mark (?) is used at the end of an asking sentence.

Write the correct punctuation marks in the story below.

Have you ever heard of John F. Kennedy   He was the youngest man ever elected president of the United States   He was also the youngest man ever to die in office

Did you know that John F. Kennedy was only 43 when he was elected president   How much older than you was he when he was elected

Kennedy had three brothers and five sisters   How would you like to have eight brothers and sisters in your family   Kennedy was born in Massachusetts, but his family moved often   Have you ever moved

Many people loved President Kennedy   It was a very sad day when he was killed   This man will never be forgotten

Try This!

Write the name of the president of the United States. Write one other fact about him.

FS-32502 Big Book of Basic Skills

Let Your Feelings Out!

Name _____

An exclamation point (!) is used at the end of an expressive sentence. These sentences show excitement, fear, or anger.

Examples ▶ *Way to go!*   *God job, Mark!*   *Hooray!*   *Oops!*

Write what you would say in each situation below. Be sure to say something expressive and use exclamation points.

1. Your team won the championship.

   _____

2. Your best friend had to give away her cat, and she is very sad.

   _____

3. Your mom just got a great new haircut.

   _____

4. Your dog just ate your book report that you worked hard on.

   _____

5. Your dad just surprised your family with a trip to the beach.

   _____

6. You just cut your finger on a knife.

   _____

7. Your brother just won first place in a spelling bee.

   _____

8. Your teacher just told your class that you are going on a picnic today.

   _____

9. Your family just won a trip to Hawaii.

   _____

10. Your little sister ruined your science project.

   _____

 **Try This!** Listen to people talk today. Write any exclamatory sentences you hear them say.

Yippee!

Name _____

An exclamation point is used at the end of an expressive sentence.

Examples *Wow!*   *I'm so happy!*   *We won!*

Write in the correct expression for each situation.

I'm so proud!	Whee! Hurry! We're late!
Way to hit that ball, Annie!	Ouch! Catch it, Joe!
Be careful, Kayla!	Oh, you poor thing!

1. _____

2. _____

3. _____

4. _____

5. _____

6. _____

7. _____

8. _____

Try This!   Draw your own scene. Write what the people are saying.
Use at least one exclamation point.

    116   FS-32502 Big Book of Basic Skills

In a Hurry!

Name _____

An abbreviation is a shortened form of a word. Abbreviations end in periods. Months of the year and the days of the week can be abbreviated.

Match each month or day of the week to its abbreviation. Then write the month or day and its abbreviation next to it.

1. Tuesday	Sun.	1.	_____
2. March	Feb.	2.	_____
3. October	Mon.	3.	_____
4. Wednesday	Sept.	4.	_____
5. January	Dec.	5.	_____
6. Sunday	Apr.	6.	_____
7. February	Mar.	7.	_____
8. September	Thurs.	8.	_____
9. November	Aug.	9.	_____
10. Monday	Nov.	10.	_____
11. August	Sat.	11.	_____
12. Saturday	Fri.	12.	_____
13. Friday	Wed.	13.	_____
14. December	Oct.	14.	_____
15. April	Jan.	15.	_____
16. Thursday	Tues.	16.	_____

Try This! Write two sentences telling about your favorite day of the week and your favorite month. Use abbreviations.

Shrink These Words

Name _____

A contraction is made when two words are combined. The apostrophe is added in place of the letter or letters that are taken away.

Examples

do not = don't
The second *o* is taken out, and an apostrophe (') is put in.

I will = I'll
The *wi* is taken out, and an apostrophe is put in.

1. would not = _____

2. are not = _____

3. does not = _____

4. is not = _____

5. could not = _____

6. should not = _____

7. he will = _____

8. they will = _____

9. it will = _____

10. she will = _____

11. we will = _____

12. you will = _____

The contractions in the sentences below are missing apostrophes. Find and circle the contractions. Write in the apostrophes.

13. Sue said shell miss the game if she doesnt hurry.

14. Well go if you want us to.

15. Itll be a fun day if we go to the beach.

16. Casey isnt riding her bike to school today.

17. I dont know if my brother is playing or not.

18. Ill help you if youll help me.

19. Wont you come to the park with me?

Try This! Find four contractions from a book. Write each contraction and the two words that make it.

FS-32502 Big Book of Basic Skills

Word Shapes

Name _____

Match the word shape contraction to the word(s) that made it.

1. cannot _____

2. does not _____

3. could not _____

4. I will _____

5. let us _____

6. you are _____

7. they are _____

8. I am _____

9. we have _____

10. she is _____

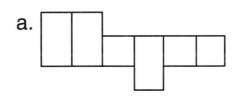

a.

b.

c.

d.

e.

f.

g.

h.

i.

j.

Try This!   Write five contractions in word shape boxes.

FS-32502 Big Book of Basic Skills

Lost and Found

Name _____

An apostrophe (') and an *s* are used to show that something belongs to someone.

Examples   *John's dog*   *Mary's book*

The items below were in the "Lost and Found" at school. Read the sentences below to help you figure out who the items belong to. Then write the person's name with an apostrophe and an *s* along with the item's name to show ownership.

1. _____   2. _____   3. _____

4. _____   5. _____   6. _____

7. _____   8. _____   9. _____

- Paul lost his book.
- Where is the backpack Peter brought?
- Katy left her lunchbox at school.
- Robin can't find her sweater.
- Beth said, "I forgot my umbrella."
- "Where did I leave my mitt?" asked Troy.
- The bat belongs to Kevin.
- Chandler can't find his shoes.
- Kara brought a new soccer ball.

Try This!   Put your name on things that belong to you. Make a list of items that you need to put your name on.

⟨120⟩

Make Me Laugh

Name _____

Quotation marks go around the words people speak. Words like *said, asked,* and *laughed* go outside the quotation marks.

Example *"I am hungry," said Bob.*

Punctuation marks like questions marks, periods, and commas go inside the quotation marks.

Write quotation marks around the words that are spoken below.

1. Do you like riddles? asked Andrew.

2. Yes, I like riddles, said Tommy.

3. What is black and white and read all over? asked Andrew.

4. A newspaper, said Tommy.

5. You're right, said Andrew.

Write seven things you have heard someone say today. Practice writing quotation marks around them.

1. _____

2. _____

3. _____

4. _____

5. _____

6. _____

7. _____

Try This! Write a riddle you know. Put quotation marks around the exact words spoken.

Dates to Remember

Name _____

A comma is used when you write a date. A comma is written between the day and the year.

Example   *March 3, 1994*

Lindsay is making a list of important dates to remember. She forgot a lot of commas between each day and the year. Write in the missing commas.

Name	Dates to Remember
Emily	Birthday—May 4 1982
Stephanie	Birthday—July 14 1986
Uncle Joe	Birthday—October 28 1963
Michael	Birthday—April 17 1994
Brittney	Birthday—March 10 1993
Grandpa	Birthday—June 6 1935; Anniversary—March 2 1958
Grandma	Birthday—May 30 1938; Anniversary—March 2 1958
Mom	Birthday—January 21 1959; Anniversary—June 4 1979
Dad	Birthday—August 9 1957; Anniversary—June 4 1979
Fluffy	Day we brought her home—December 26 1990

Make a list of important dates you need to remember below. Don't forget the commas!

1. _____
2. _____
3. _____
4. _____
5. _____

Try This!   Make a list of three important dates in your life this year. Tell why each is important.

Interesting Places

Name _____

A comma is used between a city and a state.

Examples *Atlanta, Georgia   Detroit, Michigan*

Read where the people below were born. Rewrite the names of the cities and states on the lines provided. Add commas where necessary.

1. George Washington was born in Westmoreland County Virginia.

   _____

2. Abraham Lincoln was born in Hardin Kentucky.

   _____

3. Martin Luther King, Jr. was born in Atlanta Georgia.

   _____

4. Hope Arkansas is were Bill Clinton was born.

   _____

5. East St. Louis Illinois is the birthplace of Jackie Joyner-Kersee.

   _____

6. Gertrude Stein was born in Allegheny Pennsylvania.

   _____

7. Newburgh New York is the birthplace of Geraldine Ferraro.

   _____

8. Sally Ride was born in Los Angeles California.

   _____

9. John Glenn, Jr. was born in Cambridge Ohio.

   _____

Try This! Write your name, the day and the year you were born, and where you were born.

⟨123⟩ FS-32502 Big Book of Basic Skills

Let's Have a Picnic

Name _____

Commas are used between words in a series.

Example *Alan, Kari, Sandie, Jeff, Susie, and Larry are planning a picnic.*

Below is a list of the items each child needs to bring to the picnic. Use the items in each list to write a complete sentence. Use commas between the items. The first one has been done for you.

Kari	Larry	Jeff	Sandie's mom
spoons	apples	bat	Alan
forks	grapes	ball	Kari
knives	cherries	mitt	Sandie

Alan	Sandie	Susie	Jeff's mom
soda pop	chips	tablecloth	Jeff
juice	peanuts	plates	Susie
lemonade	pretzels	napkins	Larry

1. Kari is going to bring spoons, forks, and knives.

2. Alan _____

3. Larry _____

4. Sandie _____

5. Jeff _____

6. Susie _____

7. Sandie's mom _____

8. Jeff's mom _____

Try This!

Write a sentence telling three things you would take to a picnic.

Dear Mom

Name _____

In a friendly letter, a comma is used in these places:

- between the day and the year in a date *January 6, 1997*
- at the end of the greeting *Dear Shelby,*
- at the end of the closing *Your friend,*

Read the letters below. Write in the missing commas.

1.

June 21 1997

Dear Mom

I don't think it's fair that I'm grounded for spitting food at Timmy. He deserved it! Please change your mind.

Lots of love

Joey

2.

June 22 1997

Dear Joey

Just because Timmy smashed mashed potatoes in your hair doesn't mean you can spit food at him. You're still grounded.

Lots of love

Mom

3.

June 23 1997

Dearest Mother

You look so beautiful today. I love your hair. Would you like me to wash the dishes tonight?

Your loving son

Joey

4.

June 24 1997

Dear Joey

Nice try, but you're still grounded. And yes, you may wash the dishes tonight.

Your loving mother

Mom

Try This! Write a letter to a friend. Use commas correctly. Mail the letter.

FS-32502 Big Book of Basic Skills

The Zoo

Name _____

Proofread the story below. Check off each step as you do it.

☐ Write in the four missing periods.

☐ Write in the one missing question mark.

☐ Write in the two missing commas.

☐ Write in the one missing apostrophe.

☐ Write in the two sets of missing quotation marks.

☐ Write in the one missing exclamation point.

The Zoo

Yesterday, we went to the zoo   We saw elephants   zebras and giraffes   I like the monkeys best, I said to my teacher.   What is your favorite animal   I asked her   She told me she likes giraffes the best   I think Ill go to the zoo again soon. I love it

---

Rewrite the story correctly on the lines below.
Add in all of the punctuation marks that are needed.

_____

_____

_____

_____

_____

_____

_____

Try This!

Write three sentences without any punctuation. Exchange papers with a friend. Correct each other's papers.

FS-32502 Big Book of Basic Skills

Capital Rules

Name _____

Remember, the following need to begin with capital letters:

- the first and last words and all important words in titles
- names of people, pets, and important places
- the word *I*
- the days of the week and months of the year
- street names
- the first word in each sentence.

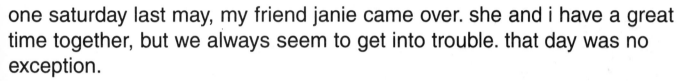

Read the story below. Circle each word that needs to begin with a capital letter. Write them on the lines below.

one saturday last may, my friend janie came over. she and i have a great time together, but we always seem to get into trouble. that day was no exception.

janie thought we should ride our bikes to the library. she wanted to get a book called *how to make a spaceship.* on our way to the library, we saw a little kitten in some woods over by pine street. It was so cute—it looked just like a little tiger.

we played with the kitten for a long time. then janie decided we should take it to my house. so we did. boy was my dad mad when he saw us coming with the little kitten and its mother running behind us! no wonder the kitten looked like a baby tiger—it was!

1. _____   8. _____   15. _____

2. _____   9. _____   16. _____

3. _____   10. _____   17. _____

4. _____   11. _____   18. _____

5. _____   12. _____   19. _____

6. _____   13. _____   20. _____

7. _____   14. _____   21. _____

Introduction

CHAPTER 5

Spelling

Spelling is a skill that is vital to everyone. It plays an important role throughout everyone's life and is used numerous times and in numerous ways on a daily basis. It is for these reasons that spelling should be an important part of all language programs.

The activities in this chapter have been designed to help students learn how to spell. They help students see patterns among groups of words. Students will gain more confidence in writing as their spelling improves and their vocabularies increase.

Below are some suggestions you might use to provide students with a complete spelling program. These suggestions, used in conjunction with the spelling list words on pages 129–158, will help all students become more confident in spelling. In some lessons, students will encounter one or more starred words. This reminds students to pay special attention to these words as they are commonly misspelled, are misused, or are words with irregular or uncommon spellings.

1. **Monday**—Present the list words. Have students write each word five times on a sheet of paper. Check the spelling or let some of your own "Super Spellers" check the other students' words. Discuss what the words have in common. **Homework:** Have students write definitions of selected words.

2. **Tuesday**—Have students do the activities featured on the activity page. You can also have students write all the words before completing the activity page so that some confidence has already been achieved. **Homework:** Have students write sentences using each of the words. Emphasize looking up any words they do not know so that no one will hand in sentences such as: *Desk. My brother is a desk.*

3. **Wednesday**—Ask students to choose two of their best sentences to read to the class. Ask the class if the sentences make sense. **Homework:** Ask students to have someone at home test them on their words.

4. **Thursday**—Ask students to write short stories using at least five of the words. Students can then exchange their stories with a friend and check each other's work. **Homework:** Have students do a final check to see if they know the words.

5. **Friday**—The Spelling Test—Dictate sentences, each containing a spelling word, to students. Explain to students that they are to write the entire sentence, complete with capitalization and proper punctuation. Ask them to underline the spelling word in each. You can either create the sentences as you give the test, or prepare them in advance. When you correct the sentences, take points off only if the spelling word itself is incorrect.

Fast Cat

Name _____

Say the words. Listen for the **short a** sound in *cat*.
The sign for **short a** is **/a/**.

cat	map	bag	sad	fast
hand	van	hat	man	can

Look at the pictures. What do you see?
Write list words to finish the sentences.

1. A _____ is in the _____ .

2. A _____ is in the _____ .

3. A _____ is in the _____ .

Change the first letter in each word to make a list word.
Write the words. Then draw a line to match each word to its picture.

4. cap   _____   •

5. dad   _____   •

6. last   _____   •

7. band   _____   •

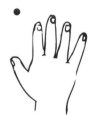

  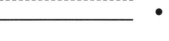

Try This!   Write a sentence. Use as many words with the **short a** sound as you can.

Wet Hen

Name_____

Say the words. Listen for the **short e** sound in *wet* and *hen*.
The sign for **short e** is **/e/**. In most of the words, **e** spells **/e/**.
In *many,* **a** spells **/e/**.

wet	ten	red	jet	leg
hen	yes	went	well	many*

Write the list word that belongs in each group.

1. boat, train, _____

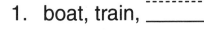

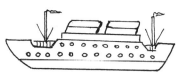

2. yellow, blue, _____

3. six, eight, _____

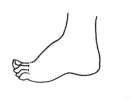

4. foot, knee, _____

5. chick, rooster, _____

Write the list words that mean the opposite.

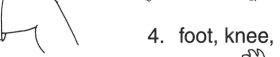

6. no _____   9. came _____

7. few _____   10. dry _____

8. sick _____

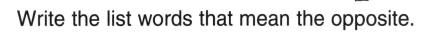

Try This!   Write as many words as you can that rhyme with *wet* and *jet.*

130

Big Pig Words

Short i sound

Name _____

Say the words. Listen for the **short i** sound in *pig*. The sign for **short i** is **/i/**. In most of the words, **i** spells **/i/**. In *been*, **ee** spells **/i/**.

big	is	it	pig	did
him	win	sit	if	been*

Write the list words in the shapes to finish the story.

Tim has a pet  . Tim calls

Tubby because he so 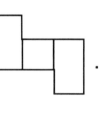 .

Tubby likes to in the mud when

 is hot. What a funny sight!

Follow the signs. Add and subtract letters. Write the list words.

1. d i g - g + d = _____

2. b e + e n d - d = _____

3. w i g - g + n = _____

4. i n - n + f = _____

Try This!   Make up your own problems for words on the list, or other words with the **short i** sound. Then ask a friend to follow the signs to figure out the words.

131   FS-32502 Big Book of Basic Skills

Frog on a Log

Name _____

Say the words. Listen for the **short o** sound in *got* and the **/ô/** sound in *log*. The sign for **short o** is **/o/**. In most of the words, **o** spells **/o/** and **/ô/**. In *want*, **a** spells **/o/**.

got	off	dog	lost	frog
pond	log	not	spot	want*

Look at the clues. Write the words to complete the puzzle.

ACROSS

2. _____ and found

4.

5.

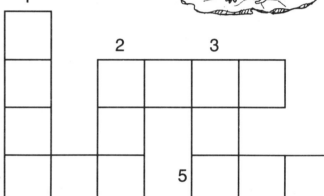

DOWN

1.

2.

3.

Add a letter to each word to make a list word. Write the word.

1. fog _____

2. go _____

3. ant _____

4. no _____

Try This!

On the back of this paper, write a story about a frog and a dog. Use as many list words as you can.

Mud on the Rug

Name _____

Say the words. Listen for the **short u** sound in *rug*. The sign for **short u** is **/u/**. In most of the words, **u** spells **/u/**. In *of* and *from*, **o** spells **/u/**.

bus	mud	run	but	rug
fun	must	stuck	of*	from*

Read the clues. Then write the list words.

1. It begins like and rhymes with . _____

2. It begins like and rhymes with . _____

3. It begins like and rhymes with . _____

Write a headline for the newspaper story.

★★ **DAILY NEWS** ★★

School _____

_____ in _____

Change one letter in *ran, if, rag,* and *most* to make list words.

 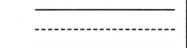

_____ _____ _____ _____

Try This! Change the **u** in *mud, but, stuck,* and *fun* to make new words. Use the back of your paper to write the words.

Play in the Rain

Name _____

Say the words. Listen for the **long a** sound in *play* and *rain*. The sign for **long a** is /ā/. In most of the words, **ay** and **ai** spell /ā/. In *they*, **ey** spells /ā/. In *said,* **ai** spells **short e**, or /e/.

| way | rain | say | wait | paint |
| train | play | today | they* | said* |

Look ↔, ↕, and ↘. Find and circle six list words.

Then write each word. Circle the letters that spell /ā/.

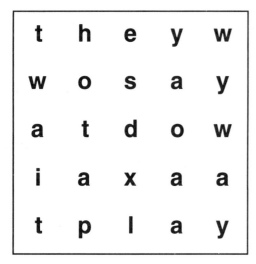

t	h	e	y	w
w	o	s	a	y
a	t	d	o	w
i	a	x	a	a
t	p	l	a	y

_____   _____

_____   _____

_____   _____

Write the list word that belongs in each group.

1. snow, hail, _____

2. bus, plane, _____

3. color, draw, _____

Write the correct list word to finish the sentence.

Run is to **ran** as **say** is to _____ .

Try This!

Finish this story: **Jay and Ray were playing outside when it started to . . .** Tell what happened. Tell what they did. Tell what they said. Underline all the **long a** words you use.

Same Name

Name_____

Say the words. Listen for the **long a** sound in *name* and *same*. The sign for **long a** is /ā/. In most of the words, **a-e** spells /ā/. In *have*, **a-e** spells **short a**, or /a/.

name	tape	bake	made	same
plate	came	ate	lake	have*

Change the order of the letters in each word in the box below to make a list word. Then use the words to finish the sentences. Hint: The two words in each sentence rhyme.

mean	eat	petal	seam

1. I _____ everything on my _____ .

2. My first _____ is the _____ as yours.

Cross out one letter in each word to make a list word.
Write the list word you make.

3. camel _____

4. baker _____

5. shave _____

6. flake _____

Add one letter to each word to make a list word. Write the word.

7. mad _____

8. tap _____

Try This! Say each pair of words: *tale/tail, made/maid.* How are they the same? How are they different? Write a sentence for each word. Use the dictionary if you need help.

Read To Me, Please

Name _____

Say the words. Listen for the **long e** sound in *read* and *me*. The sign for **long e** is /ē/. In most of the words, **ee**, **ea**, and **e** spell /ē/. In *read*, **ea** spells /ē/ or **short e**. Say *read* two ways. In *piece*, **ie** spells /ē/.

sleep	green	week	be	me
three	team	beach	read*	piece*

Write **ee**, **ea**, **ie**, or **e** to finish the words with missing letters.

1. We're going to b _____ at the b _____ch.

2. We ate gr _____n beans and a p _____ce of cheese.

3. I'm so tired I could sl _____p for a w _____k.

4. Our t _____m won by thr _____ runs.

5. Please r _____d a story to m _____.

Write the word that belongs in each group.

6. one, two, _____

7. month, day, _____

8. him, her, _____

9. shore, coast, _____

10. blue, yellow, _____

11. nap, rest, _____

12. slice, bit, _____

13. am, is, _____

Write *team* and *read*. Now switch the first and last letters. What words did you make? Write a sentence using each new word. Make sure you use them correctly.

Five to Nine

Name _____

Say the words. Listen for the **long i** sound in *five* and *nine*. The sign for **long i** is /ī/. In most of the words, **i** and **i-e** spell long i, /ī/. In *give* and *live*, **i-e** spells **short i**, or /i/.

I	time	mind	nine	kind
nice	find	five	give*	live*

Write the list words that end like 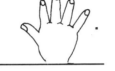 .

_____   _____   _____

1. _____   2. _____   3. _____

Write list words in the shapes to finish the sentences.

4. We had a ⬚⬚⬚⬚⬚ ⬚⬚⬚⬚ at the party.

5. Four plus ⬚⬚⬚⬚ is ⬚⬚⬚⬚ .

6. If you can't find yours, I'll ⬚⬚⬚⬚ you mine.

7. My family and ⬚ ⬚⬚⬚⬚ in a white house.

8. There was a real ⬚⬚⬚⬚ mouse in our class today!

Try This!
Change the **n** in *nice* to **m**. What word did you make?
Now change **n** to **r**, **pr**, **sl**, **sp**, and **tw** to make more new words. Use them in sentences to show what they mean.

Fly High

Name _____

Say the words. Listen for the **long i** sound in *fly* and *high*. The sign for **long i** is /ī/. In most of the words, **y** and **igh** spell /ī/. In *buy,* **uy** spells /ī/. Notice that *by* and *buy* sound the same, but they have different meanings.

my	light	fly	right	by
high	sky	night	dry	buy*

Follow the signs. Add and subtract letters to make list words.

1.   b e - e + y o u - ou = _____

2.   a s - a + k e y - e = _____

3.   o f - o + l a y - a = _____

4.   a m - a + b y - b = _____

Read each sentence. Write the list word that means the opposite of each underlined word. Circle the letters that spell /ī/ in each word.

5.   I want to <u>sell</u> that bike.   _____ •

6.   My shirt is all <u>wet</u>.   _____ •

7.   I write with my <u>left</u> hand.   _____ •

8.   We slept all <u>day</u> long.   _____ •

9.   I have <u>dark</u> brown hair.   _____ •

10.   The wall is very <u>low</u>.   _____ •

Try This!   Read a story or an article. Make a list of all the words you find with /ī/. Circle the letters that spell /ī/.

Old Home

Long o sound

Name_____

Say the words. Listen for the **long o** sound in *old* and *home*. The sign for **long o** is /ō/. In most of the words, **o** and **o-e** spell /ō/. In *come*, **o-e** spells **short u**, or /u/. In *gone*, **o-e** spells **short o**, or /o/.

no	go	home	rode	old
rope	note	open	come*	gone*

Write the list word for each clue. Then write the letters in the box to answer the riddle.

1. This is the place where you live.

2. This is a strong cord you can use to tie things.

3. This can mean *worn* or *aged*.

4. This is something you can sing or something you write.

What grows bigger the more you take away? a ___ ___ ___ ___

Circle the list word in each word. Then write the list word.

5. forgot
_____
- - - - - - - - - - - - - - - - - -
_____

6. another
_____
- - - - - - - - - - - - - - - - -
_____

7. welcome
_____
- - - - - - - - - - - - - - - -
_____

Add one letter to make a list word.

8. pen
_____
- - - - - - - - - - - - - - - -
_____

9. rod
_____
- - - - - - - - - - - - - - - -
_____

10. one
_____
- - - - - - - - - - - - - - - -
_____

Try This! You can add the letters **b**, **c**, **f**, **g**, **h**, **s**, and **t** to the beginning of one list word to make some new words. Which list word is it? What words can you make? Try to use as many of the words as you can in a silly sentence, a poem, or a story.

Row the Boat

Name _____

Say the words. Listen for the **long o** sound in *row* and *boat*. The sign for **long o** is **/ō/**. In most of the words, **ow** and **oa** spell **/ō/**. In *know*, you do not say the letter **k**.

low	road	boat	slow	snow
goat	soap	bowl	coat	know*

Answer the questions.

1. What word begins like and ends like  ? _____

2. What word begins like and ends like ? _____

3. What word begins like and ends like ? _____

4. What word begins like and ends like ? _____

5. What word begins like and ends like ? _____

Look at the five groups. Draw a line to the picture that belongs in each group. Then write the word for each picture.

6.

7. _____

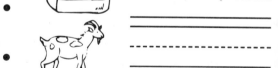

8. _____

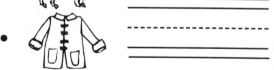

9. _____

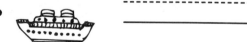  _____

10. _____

Try This!

Make up a silly story about a goat. Use as many of the list words as you can. Then draw a picture to illustrate your story.

FS-32502 Big Book of Basic Skills

School Rule

Name_____

Say the words. Listen for the vowel sound in *school* and *rule.* The sign for this sound is **/ü/**. The sound **/ü/** can be spelled **oo** and **u-e**.

rule	school	too	cool	soon
loose	tune	zoo	boot	flute

Write two list words to complete each sentence. Circle the letters that spell **/ü/**.

1. If we don't leave _____ , we'll be late for _____ .

2. A moose got _____ in the _____ .

3. Listen to the _____ I can play on my _____ .

Write the list word for each clue. The letters in the boxes form another word with the vowel sound **/ü/**.

4. It sounds just like  .

5. It begins like  .

6. It ends like 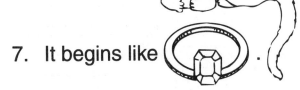 .

7. It begins like 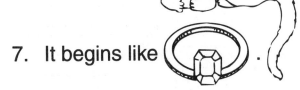 .

Try This!

Read this sentence: **Do you know who has a new blue suit?** Underline all the words with the **/ü/** sound. Notice how the **/ü/** sound is spelled.

   FS-32502 Big Book of Basic Skills

Let's Eat Cake!

/k/ sound

Name_____

Say the words. Listen for the sounds of /k/ in *cake.*
The /k/ sound can be spelled **c**, **k**, and **ck**.

Write a list word to answer each question.
Then circle the letters that spell /k/ in each word.

kid	pick
corn	clock
kite	black
cake	lock
rock	cook

1. What grows ears but cannot hear? _____

2. What lets you know the time? _____

3. What can you fly in the sky? _____

4. What is the color of coal? _____

5. What can you make with
   flour, eggs, and sugar? _____

6. What do you call a young goat? _____

Look at each word below. Find, circle, and write the list word hidden in
each word. Then draw a line to the picture of each list word.

7. cookie _____ •

8. rocket _____ •

9. block _____ •

10. pickle _____ •

Try This! Say this sentence five times as fast as you can: **Peter Piper
picked a peck of pickled peppers**. Which words have the /k/
sound? Make up your own tongue twister using list words.

142   FS-32502 Big Book of Basic Skills

/sn/, /sl/, /st/, /sp/
sounds

Snap Your Fingers!

Name _____

Say the words. Listen for the two sounds that begin each word as in *snap*.
The signs **/sn/**, **/sl/**, **/st/**, and **/sp/** stand for the sounds you hear.
The word *speak* is like the word *spoke*. *Speak* means you are talking now.
Spoke means you have already talked. The word *slept* is like the word *sleep*.
Sleep means you are resting now. *Slept* means you have already rested.

snap	sled	stop	story	speak
slide	state	snake	slept*	spoke*

Write the list words that have the words below in them.

_____   _____   _____

1. ate _____   2. lid _____   3. nap _____

Write the list word that has the same meaning as the underlined word in
each sentence.

4. My friend wants to <u>talk</u> with me.

5. We <u>talked</u> for over an hour.

6. I just read the funniest <u>tale</u>.

7. The baby <u>napped</u> for two hours.

Write the list word that rhymes with the word for each picture.

8.    9. 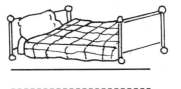   10.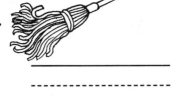

Try This!

Make a chart. Find and list other words that begin with the **/sn/**,
/sl/, **/st/**, and **/sp/** sounds. Then write silly sentences using as
many words as you can with the same beginning sounds.

Pass the Bread!

Name _____

Say the words. Listen for the two sounds that begin each word as in *bread.* The signs **/br/**, **/fr/**, **/cl/**, and **/pl/** stand for the sounds you hear. In *bread,* **ea** spells **short e**, or **/e/**. In *friend,* **ie** spells **/e/**.

clean	bring	Friday	plane	class
free	please	plant	bread*	friend*

Read the clues. Write the list words.

1. It begins like  and ends like  . _____

2. It begins like  and ends like  . _____

3. It begins like and ends like . _____

4. It begins like and ends like . _____

Write the list words to finish the sentences. Hint: Each list word rhymes with an underlined word.

5. Would you _____ pass the <u>cheese</u>.

6. Do you want to go by <u>train</u> or by _____?

7. We have <u>three</u> _____ tickets to the movies.

8. I dropped a <u>glass</u> jar in _____ today.

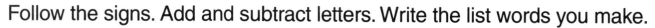

Follow the signs. Add and subtract letters. Write the list words you make.

9. fry - y + pie - p + and - a = _____

10. bar - a + sea - s + d = _____

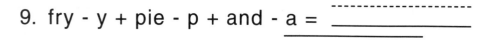

Try This! Think of other words that begin with **br**, **fr**, **cl**, and **pl**. Make up sentences with rhyming words or problems for your classmates to solve.

FS-32502 Big Book of Basic Skills

/är/ sound

Dark Car

Name _____

Say the words. Listen for the vowel sound with **r** as in *dark* and *car.*
The sign for this sound is **/är/**. In most of the words, **ar** spells **/är/**.
The word *are* has the **/är/** sound, but don't forget the **e.** In
warm, **ar** spells the vowel sound with **r** as in *for.*

car	farm
part	large
far	start
hard	dark
are*	warm*

Write the list word that means the opposite of the
underlined word in each sentence. Then reread the
sentences using the list words. _____

1. I have to <u>finish</u> my homework. _____

2. This bread is very <u>soft</u>. _____

3. Our puppy is very <u>small</u>. _____

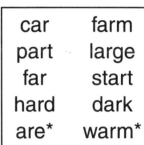

4. How <u>cool</u> the weather is today! _____

5. I have a <u>light</u> blue coat and hat. _____

6. Our house is quite <u>near</u>. _____

Write the list word to finish each sentence.

7. Our family lives on a dairy _____ .

8. Where did you park the _____ ?

9. Which _____ of the story did you like?

10. What _____ your favorite television shows?

Try This! Pretend you are visiting a farm. Describe what you see.
Use as many list words as you can.

Worms in the Dirt

Name _____

Say the words. Listen for the **vowel sound with r** as in *worm* and *dirt*.
The sign for this sound is **/ėr/**. The **/ėr/** sound can be spelled **ir**, **er**, **ur**,
and **or**.

girl	her	turn	work	first
hurt	dirt	shirt	worm	jerk

Use the words in the box to fill in the blanks.

hurt
her
girl
dirt
shirt

_____
The little _____ who fell in the

_____   _____
_____ is crying. She _____

_____   _____
_____ knee and ripped her _____ .

Write **er**, **ur**, **ir**, or **or** to finish the words with missing letters.

1. Is it your t _____ n or mine?

2. The bird caught a w_____m.

3. The old truck started with a j_____k.

4. What is your f_____st name?

5. We have a lot of w_____k to do.

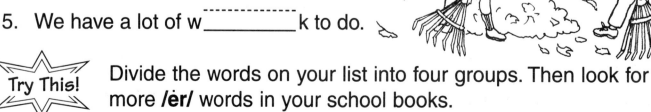

Try This! Divide the words on your list into four groups. Then look for
more **/ėr/** words in your school books.

⟨146⟩

Final /st/, /sk/,
/nd/, /mp/ sounds

Listen to This

Name _____

Say the words. Listen for the two sounds that end each word.
The signs **/st/**, **/sk/**, **/nd/**, and **/mp/** stand for the sounds you hear.

The first pair of words gives you a clue about how the second pair of
words go together. Write the list word that belongs in each blank.

jump
last
sand
desk
stand
best
camp
ask
behind
mask

1. **smallest** and **biggest**, **worst** and _____

2. **take** and **give**, **answer** and _____

3. **right** and **left**, **ahead** and _____

4. **come** and **go**, **sit** and _____

How does each word end? Draw a line to make a match. Then write the
word. Next, draw a line to match each word and picture.

5. j u •   • n d _____ •

6. s a •   • s k _____ •

7. d e •   • m p _____ •

Change one letter of each word to make a list word. Write the word.

8. came

9. mark

10. lost

Pretend you are at a summer camp. Write a letter to a friend.
Use as many of the list words as you can to tell all about it.

FS-32502 Big Book of Basic Skills

Hear It Here!

Name _____

Some words sound the same, but they have different spellings and meanings. Say the pairs of words below.

hear	our	won	for	ate
here	hour	one	four	eight

Look at each pair of words. Write the correct words in the blanks to finish the sentences.

four
for

1. I have _____ books _____ you.

one
won

2. Our baseball team _____ by _____ run.

ate
eight

3. We _____ breakfast at _____ o'clock.

here
hear

4. I can't _____ you from _____ .

hour
our

5. We have an _____ to do _____ homework.

Look ↔, ↕, and ↘. Circle five list words hidden in the puzzle. Then write the list word that sounds the same as each word you find.

h	o	n	f
o	e	u	o
n	o	r	r
e	a	t	e

_____ _____

_____ _____

_____ _____

_____ _____

_____ _____

Try This!

Write three more pairs of words that sound the same but are spelled differently.

Look at This Tooth!

Name _____

Say the words. Listen for the sound that the letters **th** make in *this* and *tooth*. Circle the letters **th** in each list word. Notice that some words begin or end with **th**. Some words have **th** in the middle.

than	the	thank	then	mother
this	that	tooth	with	father

Write the list word that rhymes with the underlined word in each sentence.

1. Did you _____ your Uncle <u>Hank</u>?

2. Mrs. <u>Smith</u> is coming _____ us.

3. My <u>brother</u> Mike helped our _____ .

4. My sister <u>Ruth</u> lost her first _____ .

5. Dad <u>ran</u> faster _____ Mom.

6. "Please don't <u>bother</u>," said my _____ .

Add one letter to each word to make a list word. Write the words.

7. he _____

8. his _____

9. the _____

10. hat _____

Try This! Make a list of other words that have **th** at the beginning, in the middle, and at the end. Say each word. Listen for the sound **th** makes.

FS-32502 Big Book of Basic Skills

White Whale

Name _____

Say the words. Listen for the sounds that the letters **wh** make in *white* and *whale.* Most of the list words have the same beginning sound that you hear in *white* and *whale.* In *who* and *whose,* **wh** has the sound of **/h/** as in *hat.*

which	what	where	why	when
whale	white	wheel	who*	whose*

Name each picture. Then write the list word that has the picture's name in it.

1. _____   2. _____   3. _____

Name each picture. Write the list word that rhymes with it.

4. _____   5. _____   6. _____

Write the list word that correctly completes each sentence.

7. Do you know _____ my book is?

8. Do you know _____ book this is?

9. Do you know _____ of the books is yours?

10. Do you know _____ has my book?

Try This! Make a list of questions about such things as books, school, sports, TV programs, movies, and games using as many list words as you can. Then have a friend answer your questions.

Cheese Shop

Name _____

Say the words. Listen for the sounds that begin the words *cheese* and *shop.* The signs for the sounds you hear are **/ch/** and **/sh/**. Underline the letters **ch** and **sh** in the list words. Notice that some words begin with **/ch/** and **/sh/**, and some words end with **/ch/** and **/sh/**.

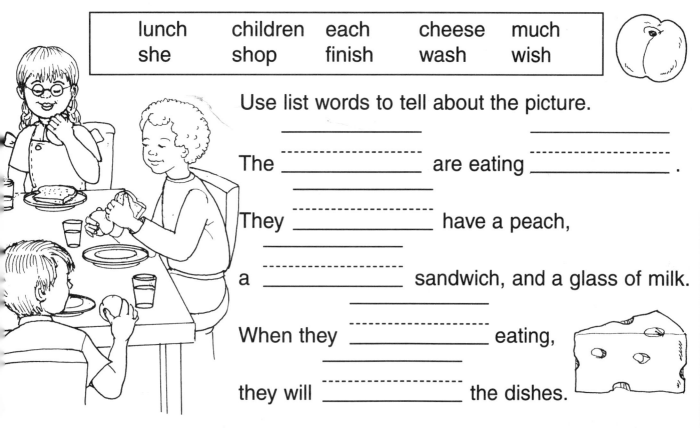

lunch	children	each	cheese	much
she	shop	finish	wash	wish

Use list words to tell about the picture.

The _____ are eating _____ .

They _____ have a peach,

a _____ sandwich, and a glass of milk.

When they _____ eating,

they will _____ the dishes.

Read the sentences. The underlined words are not spelled correctly. How should they be spelled? Write the words correctly.

1. My sister needs to <u>chop</u> for a new pair of shoes. _____

2. "I <u>wich</u> you would help me choose," <u>che</u> said. _____

3. "I hope they don't cost too <u>mush</u>," I said. _____

Try This! Pretend you are going to the mall to shop. Make a list of all the things you can buy that begin with **ch** and **sh**.

Brown House

/ou/ soun

Name _____

Say the words. Listen for the vowel sound that you hear in the middle of *brown* and *house.* The sign for the sound you hear is **/ou/**. In the list words, underline the letters **ou** and **ow**. They spell **/ou/**.

brown	now	sound	town	round
down	loud	owl	out	house

Write **ou** or **ow** to finish the words in the sentences. Then write the words on the lines to the right.

1. We live in a br_____n and white h_____se.

   It is in the middle of t_____n.

2. What was that l_____d s_____nd?

   Don't worry. It was just an _____l.

Read the clues. Write the words.

3. not square but   __ __ __ __

4. not in, but __

5. not ↑, but __

6. Write the letters in the boxes to make a list word. _____

Try This!   Write a poem about a house using as many of the list words as you can.

⟨152⟩   FS-32502 Big Book of Basic Skills

i/ sound

Look in the Bush

Name _____

Say the words. Listen for the vowel sound that you hear in the middle of *look* and *bush*. The sign for the sound you hear is /ủ/. In the list words, underline the letters **oo** and **u**. They spell /ủ/.

Write the list words in the shapes to finish the sentences.

bush
push
pull
put
full
foot
took
good
book
look

1. Take a [⌐_⌐] over there.

2. Do you see the bird's nest in the [⌐_⌐] ?

3. I just finished reading this [⌐_⌐] .

4. It was really very [⌐_⌐] .

Write the list word that means the same as the underlined word(s) in each sentence.

5. <u>Place</u> the cans and boxes in the bag.   _____

6. Grab the rope and <u>tug</u> as hard as you can.   _____

7. <u>Press hard</u> on the door to open it.   _____

Change one letter to make a list word.

8. fort _____   9. fell _____   10. tool _____

Try This! Read this group of words: *moon, wood, noon, cook, root, hook*. How are they alike and different? Write a sentence for each word.

Silly Puppy

Name _____

Say the words. Notice that each word has two parts, or syllables, and each part has a vowel sound. Listen for the **long e** sound, or /ē/, as in *silly* and *puppy*, at the end of each word. In all the words, **y** spells /ē/. In *easy,* **ea** spells /ē/ in the first syllable, and the **s** sounds like **z**. In *pretty,* **e** spells /i/.

carry	penny	funny	only	very
baby	puppy	happy	easy*	pretty*

Write the list word to finish each sentence.

I have a _____ sister.

She is _____ one month

old. I have to be _____

careful when I hold her.

Find each word below in a list word. Write the list word. Then circle the double letters in the middle of each word you write.

1. car _____

2. up _____

3. fun _____

4. pen _____

Read the clues. Write the list words.

5. not sad _____

6. not hard _____

7. not ugly _____

Try This! Write a sentence using as many of the list words as you can. Then draw a picture about your sentence.

FS-32502 Big Book of Basic Skill

Peaches, Pears, Cherries

Name _____

Say the words. Each word names more than one of something. You add **-s** to some words like *pear* to name more than one. You add **-es** to some words like *peach* to name more than one. You change **y** to **i** before adding **-es** to some words like *cherry* to name more than one.

pears	beets	beans	eggs	peaches
dishes	berries	boxes	meats	cherries

Write list words to complete the sentences.

1. Two kinds of vegetables are _____ and _____ .

2. Ham, chicken, and beef are _____ .

3. Peaches, pears, and _____ all grow on trees.

Write the list words not used above. Then find and circle each word that names one of them in the puzzle.

p	e	a	r	z
b	e	r	r	y
e	o	a	m	q
g	z	x	c	u
g	d	i	s	h

4. _____   7. _____

5. _____   8. _____

6. _____   9. _____

Try This!

Read a news article, a story, or a few pages from a textbook. Make a list of 10 words you find that name more than one. Then write the word for only one of each thing.

Hop, Hop, Hopping

Name _____

Say the words. Listen for the short vowel sounds. Next, look at the words with the **-ing** and **-ed** endings. Then look at the words without the endings. See what happens to the final consonant when **-ing** and **-ed** are added. The final consonant is doubled when **-ing** and **-ed** are added. In the list words, underline the double letters.

hug	hop	step	tap	rip
hugged	hopping	stepped	tapping	ripped

Write a list word to finish each sentence.

1. The baby _____ his teddy bear.

2. The boy _____ over the puddle.

3. I _____ my jacket the other day.

4. Who is _____ on the window?

5. I am _____ like a frog!

Cross out one letter in each word to make a list word. Write the word.

6. tape _____ 7. hope _____ 8. ripe _____

Change one letter in each word to make a list word. Write the word.

9. mug _____ 10. stop _____

Try This! Add **-ing** to *hug, step,* and *rip.* Add **-ed** to *hop* and *tap.* Then write a sentence for each word you make.

〈156〉

Compound words

Put Two Together

Name _____

Say the words. Listen for the two words that make up each word as in *backpack*. The list words are called **compound words**. Circle the two words in each compound word below.

without	inside	bedroom	backpack	homework
anyone	something	sunlight	football	everyday

Find a word in List A that goes with a word in List B to make a list word. Then write the words.

A	B
any	day
every	thing
some	one

1. _____   2. _____   3. _____

Write the list word that begins and ends like each word.

4. wet _____   5. sit _____   6. feel _____

Write a list word to finish each sentence.

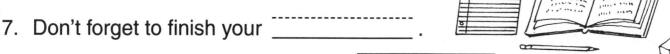

7. Don't forget to finish your _____ .

8. There's a sandwich and fruit in my _____ .

9. The _____ of my coat is blue.

10. I have to clean up my _____ today.

Try This!   Make other compound words using the words that make up the compound words on your list. For example, the words in *without* and *inside* can be used to make *within* and *outside*.

Do Not! Don't!

Name _____

Say the words. Notice the special mark in *don't.* All the list words are contractions. A **contraction** is a word made from two words, but one or more letters are left out. An apostrophe (') takes the place of the letters that are left out. The word *don't* is a contraction for *do* and *not.* The apostrophe takes the place of the **o** in *not.*

I'm	don't	it's	we're	isn't
can't	you'll	they're	what's	haven't

Write the contraction for the underlined words in the sentences.

1. Dad says <u>it is</u> time for dinner. _____

2. Do you know what <u>we are</u> having? _____

3. <u>You will</u> never guess. _____

4. We <u>have not</u> had fish for awhile. _____

5. I <u>do not</u> like fish very much. _____

6. <u>What is</u> for dessert? _____

Write the list words to finish the paragraph.

_____ _____

_____ really upset! I _____ find my books anywhere.

I think _____ in my backpack, but my backpack _____

anywhere to be found either!

Try This! Make a list of all the contractions you use. Write the two words that make up each contraction. Then compare the contractions on your list with the contractions on a friend's list.

CHAPTER 6

Vocabulary Development

Vocabulary is fundamental to every aspect of language; listening, speaking, reading, and writing. These basic language skills are built upon students' knowledge of and control over words. It is clear that the teaching of vocabulary is crucial to helping students become confident users of the English language.

A student who is first entering school may have a vocabulary of about 3,000 to 4,000 words; by the time he or she completes college, his or her vocabulary may have increased to well over 10,000 words. As a student's vocabulary grows, so does his or her ability to comprehend spoken and written language. In turn, a child is better able to express his or her own thoughts and ideas to others.

The activities in this chapter have been designed to help increase students' vocabularies and to develop in students a greater understanding and appreciation of the English language. The activities were created to help students feel comfortable and confident about building their vocabularies. In order to ensure success, students must be guided through the activities presented.

A variety of fun and simple formats are included throughout the chapter. Students will enjoy solving codes, puzzles, and riddles; using context clues; and completing stories and sentences.

The activities can be used alone or as an integral part of any language program. They can also be used in conjunction with literature-based programs to provide students with the benefits of a well-rounded English language education.

At the Beach

Name_____

Word Box

shells   dunes   ocean   beach   waves   tide   vacation

Complete the sentences with words from the Word Box.

1. The beach is a great place to take a ___ ___ ___ ___ ___ ___ ___ ___.

2. Huge sand ___ ___ ___ ___ ___ pile up from heavy winds.

3. I take walks and collect sea ___ ___ ___ ___ ___ ___.

4. When the ___ ___ ___ ___ is out, I go into the ocean.

5. I like to try to catch the ___ ___ ___ ___ ___.

6. At night, the ___ ___ ___ ___ ___ looks dark and smooth.

7. I love to go to the ___ ___ ___ ___ ___ on my vacation!

Try This!

Write a story about an adventure that might happen at the beach.

FS-32502 Big Book of Basic Skill

Months of the Year

Name _____

Use the code to write the months in the shapes in which they belong.

A	B	C	D	E	F	G	H	I	J	K	L	M
1	2	3	4	5	6	7	8	9	10	11	12	13

N	O	P	Q	R	S	T	U	V	W	X	Y	Z
14	15	16	17	18	19	20	21	22	23	24	25	26

___ ___ ___ ___ ___ ___ ___ ___
4 5 3 5 13 2 5 18

___ ___ ___ ___ ___ ___ ___
10 1 14 21 1 18 25

___ ___ ___ ___ ___ ___ ___ ___
6 5 2 18 21 1 18 25

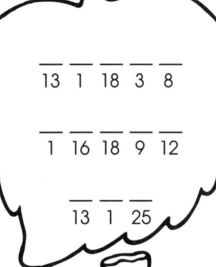

___ ___ ___ ___ ___
13 1 18 3 8

___ ___ ___ ___ ___
1 16 18 9 12

___ ___ ___
13 1 25

___ ___ ___ ___
10 21 14 5

___ ___ ___ ___
10 21 12 25

___ ___ ___ ___ ___ ___
1 21 7 21 19 20

___ ___ ___ ___ ___ ___ ___ ___ ___
19 5 16 20 5 13 2 5 18

___ ___ ___ ___ ___ ___ ___
15 3 20 15 2 5 18

___ ___ ___ ___ ___ ___ ___ ___
14 15 22 5 13 2 5 18

Try This! Write the months of the year in order starting with January.

〈161〉

Decade Numbers

Name _____

Count by tens to find the number of marbles in each group. Write the number on the line. Use the words in the box to help you.

10 ten	20 twenty	30 thirty
40 forty	50 fifty	60 sixty
70 seventy	80 eighty	90 ninety

1.

_____

2.

_____

3.

_____

4.

_____

5.

_____

6.

_____

7.

_____

8.

_____

9.

_____

 **Try This!** Write the decade number words from ten to ninety in order.

FS-32502 Big Book of Basic Skills

VOCAB. DEV.

School Helpers

Name _____

Use the code to write the name of each school helper described below.

A	B	C	D	E	F	G	H	I	J	K	L	M
1	2	3	4	5	6	7	8	9	10	11	12	13
N	O	P	Q	R	S	T	U	V	W	X	Y	Z
14	15	16	17	18	19	20	21	22	23	24	25	26

1. The __ __ __ __ __ __ __ __ __ is the head of the school.
   16 18 9 14 3 9 16 1 12

2. The __ __ __ __ __ __ __ __ __ knows where the books are.
   12 9 2 18 1 18 9 1 14

3. The __ __ __ __ __ __ __ __ __ keeps the building clean.
   3 21 19 20 15 4 9 1 14

4. The __ __ __ __ __ __ __ __ __ runs the office smoothly.
   19 5 3 18 5 20 1 18 25

5. The __ __ __ __ __ works in the health room.
   14 21 18 19 5

6. My __ __ __ __ __ __ __ works with me every day.
   20 5 1 3 8 5 18

Try This! Use the code to write a sentence about a school helper. Ask a friend to solve it.

FS-32502 Big Book of Basic Skills

Cooking Class

Name _____

Sometimes you look at a **recipe** when cooking something new. First, you must get all the **ingredients** needed to make the dish. If the food will be served hot, you may need to **bake** or **broil** it in the **oven**. Maybe you will **boil** something in a pot on the **stove**. If the food is served cold, you will need to put it in the **refrigerator**. Following a new recipe may not be easy, but it is always fun!

Write the **boldfaced** word from the story to complete each sentence.

1. Food is kept cold in a __ __ __ __ __ __ __ __ __ __ __ __.

2. The __ __ __ __ __ __ __ __ __ __ __ are all the things needed to make a recipe.

3. You may __ __ __ __ something in a pot.

4. Food is boiled on a __ __ __ __ __.

5. You can __ __ __ __ or __ __ __ __ __ food that is served hot.

6. Food is baked or broiled in an __ __ __ __.

7. The directions for making a food dish is the __ __ __ __ __ __.

Write two of the **boldfaced** words from the story in a sentence.

_____

_____

Try This!   Write a recipe for making a peanut butter and jelly sandwich.

Dollars and Cents

Name _____

Use words from the Word Box to complete the riddles.

Word Box

half-dollar   dollar   quarter   dime   nickel   penny

1. I am worth 1¢.
   I am smaller than a nickel.
   What coin am I?

   _____

2. I am the largest coin.
   I am worth 50¢.
   What coin am I?

   _____

3. I am the smallest coin.
   I am worth 10¢.
   What coin am I?

   _____

4. I am worth $\frac{1}{4}$ of a dollar.
   I am larger than a nickel.
   What coin am I?

   _____

5. I am larger than a penny.
   I am worth 5¢.
   What coin am I?

   _____

6. I am worth more than any coin.
   I am made of paper.
   What am I?

   _____

Try This! Write the names of the coins in order from least to greatest in value.

Plant Parts

Name _____

Some plant parts are labeled below.

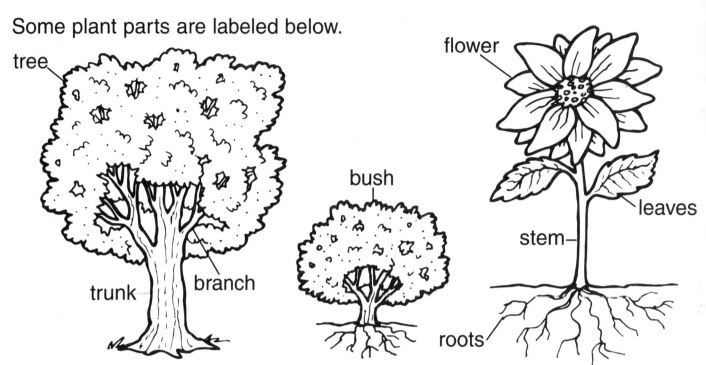

Circle the labeled words in the puzzle. The words go across and down.

```
w  x  c  r  z  a  m  r  b  l  b  u  s  h  x  x
u  t  t  a  l  w  a  t  x  c  r  r  n  q  q  f
r  r  d  d  e  g  r  r  e  n  s  t  e  m  l  l
p  u  b  l  a  b  k  e  g  r  e  d  r  n  g  o
l  n  l  c  v  r  a  e  e  l  l  o  o  x  f  w
e  k  a  a  e  p  l  e  x  x  c  n  w  k  t  e
x  x  h  m  s  e  b  r  a  n  c  h  n  h  k  r
c  s  k  x  i  r  o  o  t  s  n  g  e  e  r  r
```

 **Try This!**   List the names of five plants you know.

Days of the Week

Name_____

Read each riddle. Unscramble the words shown to find the
answers. Use the words in the Word Box to help.

Word Box

Sunday

Monday

Tuesday

Wednesday

Thursday

Friday

Saturday

1. Tomorrow will be Monday.
   What is today? (unSyda) _____

2. Tomorrow will be Wednesday.
   What is today? (uTyades) _____

3. Yesterday was Thursday.
   What is today? (rdiFya) _____

4. Today is Sunday.
   What was yesterday? (dySaurta) _____

5. Today is Tuesday.
   What was yesterday? (Myadon) _____

6. Today is Wednesday.
   What will tomorrow be? (rsuThyad) _____

7. Today is Thursday.
   What was yesterday? (dnyasdeeW)_____

Try This!

What day is it today? Write it. Then write what day it was
yesterday and what day it will be tomorrow.

FS-32502 Big Book of Basic Skills

Animals and Their Young

Name _____

Read the first animal name in each pair. Unscramble the second word to find out what that animal's young is called. Use the words in the box to help you.

calf	pup
duckling	kitten
joey	cub
foal	chick

1. kangaroo, ejyo

   _____

2. cat, tnietk

   _____

3. wolf, ppu

   _____

4. duck, cluignkd

   _____

5. horse, loaf

   _____

6. elephant, falc

   _____

7. bear, bcu

   _____

8. sea bird, kihcc

   _____

Try This! Write the baby animal names in alphabetical order.

In the City

Name _____

Read this story about a visit to the city. Then answer the questions.

Last spring, I finally got to visit a big city. Most of the **skyscrapers** I saw were over 60 stories high! The streets were crowded with people **bustling** everywhere. At night, the streetlights **illuminated** the streets, giving the city a party **atmosphere**. I enjoyed my trip to the city.

1. Which **boldfaced** word in the story means:

   a. tall buildings _____

   b. rushing around _____

   c. lit up _____

   d. a feeling in the air around you _____

2. Write your own sentences using the words below.

   atmosphere _____

   _____

   bustling _____

   _____

   skyscrapers _____

   _____

   illuminated _____

   _____

Try This!   Draw a picture of a large city. Write three words to describe it.

Polygons

Name _____

A **polygon** is a shape with three or more sides.

Each picture below shows a different polygon and its name.
Draw a line to match each polygon to its definition.

1. hexagon  polygon with 3 sides

2. pentagon polygon with 5 sides

3. octagon polygon with 7 sides

4. heptagon polygon with 4 sides

5. quadrilateral  polygon with 6 sides

6. triangle polygon with 8 sides

Try This!

Make a design using three different types of polygons. Write the words that describe the polygons you use.

FS-32502 Big Book of Basic Skills

It All Adds Up

Name _____

Find the **boldfaced** words in the puzzle. The words go across and down.

1. To find a **sum**, you must **add**.
2. To find a **difference**, you must **subtract**.
3. The numbers 1, 3, 5, and 7 are **odd**.
4. The numbers 2, 4, 6, and 8 are **even**.
5. 27 is **greater** than 23.
6. 56 is **less** than 70.
7. An **hour** is 60 **minutes**.

```
w x m r z a m r b l b o d x x
u t i a l w s u m c r r n h q m
s r n d e g r r l e s s e o l i
u a u a a g k e g r e d r u g p
b n t d m r r m e l l o o r f i
t k e d e e l e s x c n z k t o
r x s m s a d i f f e r e n c e
a s k x i t o m t s n g e e r s
c x h m s e b r e v e n n h k r
t y e d a r s w t s n g p a r o
```

Try This! Write a paragraph using five of the math words from above.

FS-32502 Big Book of Basic Skills

All in the Family

Using a code

Name _____

Use the code to write the name of each family member below.

A	B	C	D	E	F	G	H	I	J	K	L	M
1	2	3	4	5	6	7	8	9	10	11	12	13

N	O	P	Q	R	S	T	U	V	W	X	Y	Z
14	15	16	17	18	19	20	21	22	23	24	25	26

1. The brother of your mother or father is your __ __ __ __ __.
   21 14 3 12 5

2. The sister of your mother or father is your __ __ __ __.
   1 21 14 20

3. The children of your aunts and uncles are your __ __ __ __ __ __ __.
   3 15 21 19 9 14 19

4. Your mom or dad's mother is your __ __ __ __ __ __ __ __ __ __ __.
   7 18 1 14 4 13 15 20 8 5 18

5. Your mom or dad's father is your __ __ __ __ __ __ __ __ __ __ __ __.
   7 18 1 14 4 6 1 20 8 5 18

6. A girl is a __ __ __ __ __ __ __ __.
   4 1 21 7 8 20 5 18

7. A boy is a __ __ __.
   19 15 14

Try This! Write the names of your relatives using the code. Tell how you are related to them.

FS-32502 Big Book of Basic Skills

What's the Order?

Name _____

first   second   third   fourth   fifth   sixth   seventh   eighth   ninth   tenth

Complete the sentences using the ordinal numbers above.

1. The koala is _____ .

2. The monkey is _____ .

3. The kangaroo is _____ .

4. The elephant is _____ .

5. The crane is _____ .

6. The giraffe is _____ .

7. The zebra is _____ .

8. The tiger is _____ .

9. The lion is _____ .

10. The fox is _____ .

Try This!   List the animals as they would be standing in line from first to tenth.

FS-32502 Big Book of Basic Skills

Sound-Check

Name _____

Some words sound alike but have different meanings and spellings.

Complete the sentences using the correct words from the Word Box.

1. I went _____ the store and bought _____ apples.

2. My brother _____ five cookies and left _____ cookies for the rest of the family.

3. The kind _____ at the hotel _____ the bed.

4. I didn't _____ my teacher telling the class to "Come _____ ."

5. Did you _____ the dolphin in the _____ ?

Word Box

made

see

hear

to

eight

two

here

sea

maid

ate

Try This!   Write the words from the Word Box in pairs of sound-alike words.

FS-32502 Big Book of Basic Skills

Happy Holidays

Name _____

Read this story about holidays. Then answer the questions.

In November, many people in the United States celebrate **Thanksgiving**. On this holiday, people give thanks for what they have. Thanksgiving always falls on the fourth Thursday in November. **Hanukkah**, **Kwanzaa**, and **Christmas** are all celebrated in December. All three of these holidays are happy, festive occasions. On May 5, **Cinco de Mayo** is celebrated with parades and parties.

1. Which **boldfaced** word describes a holiday celebrated in November?

    _____

2. Which **boldfaced** words describe holidays celebrated in December?

    _____   _____

    _____

3. Which **boldfaced** words describe a holiday celebrated in May?

    _____

4. Does everyone in the world celebrate Thanksgiving? _____

5. Is Cinco de Mayo always celebrated in May? _____

6. Is Christmas the only holiday in December? _____

7. What is your favorite holiday? _____

    Why is it your favorite? _____

    _____

Try This! List other holidays that you celebrate. Write a sentence describing each holiday.

Magnets

Name _____

Use the words in the Word Box to fill in the missing word in each sentence.

Word Box

positive	charges	negative	poles	magnets	repel

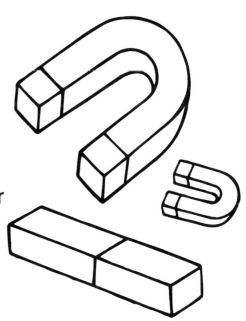

○_ _ _ _ _ _ are objects that can attract other objects. Magnets have two

_ _ _○_ _, one on each end. One pole is

_ _ _ _○_ _ _ and is marked with a

(+). The other pole is _ _ _○_ _ _ _

and is marked with a (–). Two positive charges or

two negative charges push away from each

other, or _ _ _ _○_. Positive and negative

_ _ _ _ _ _○ attract, or draw toward,

each other.

What may be attracted to a magnet? Find out by writing the circled letters

in the order that they appear above.   _ _ _ _ _ _ _

Try This!   Write the words from the Word Box in alphabetical order.

Our Earth

Name _____

Read this story about our Earth. The **boldfaced** words may be new to you. Their meanings are given below the story. Write the word that matches each meaning.

We need to **protect** the Earth so it lasts longer. To do this, we can stop **polluting** our oceans and land areas. We can **recycle** plastics, metals, and glass. We can **conserve** by using **solar energy** for heating. If we all work hard, our Earth will be safe to live in for millions of years.

1. Energy from the sun _____

2. Take care of something _____

3. To save _____

4. Use over and over _____

5. Making something dirty or unsafe for use _____

Do the pictures below show **polluting** or **recycling**? Write the word below the picture.

6.

7.

_____   _____

Try This!   What can YOU do to help our Earth?

FS-32502 Big Book of Basic Skills

In the Library

Name _____

Use the code to write the different types of books below.

A	B	C	D	E	F	G	H	I	J	K	L	M
1	2	3	4	5	6	7	8	9	10	11	12	13

N	O	P	Q	R	S	T	U	V	W	X	Y	Z
14	15	16	17	18	19	20	21	22	23	24	25	26

1.

The Life of George Washington

__ __ __ __ __ __ __ __ __
2 9 15 7 18 1 16 8 25

2.

Learning About the Moon and Sun

__ __ __ __ __ __ __
19 3 9 5 14 3 5

3.

Life in the Early Days of America

__ __ __ __ __ __ __
8 9 19 20 15 18 25

4.

Stuart Little

__ __ __ __ __ __ __
6 9 3 20 9 15 14

5.

The True Book of Facts and Lists

__ __ __ __ __ __ __ __ __ __
14 15 14 6 9 3 20 9 15 14

Go to the library. Write a title for each type of book above.

Lots of Languages

Name _____

Use the chart to help you complete the paragraph.

Country	Language Spoken
France	French
Greece	Greek
Israel	Hebrew
Italy	Italian
Mexico	Spanish
United States of America	English

   Most people in the United States of America speak _____ .

In Mexico, most people speak _____ . People in Israel speak

_____ . In Greece, people speak _____ . The main

language spoken in Italy is _____ . People in France speak

_____ .

Unscramble to write the name of each language.

1. GESLINH

2. PHSSAIN

3. CFENHR

_____

_____

_____

4. WREBHE

5. KERGE

6. INATLIA

_____

_____

_____

Try This!

Make scrambled words for other languages. Ask a classmate
to unscramble them.

FS-32502 Big Book of Basic Skills

Take Part

Name _____

Read these different meanings for the word *part*.

A) a necessary piece
B) a portion or share
C) a role in a play
D) a dividing line formed in combing hair
E) to break or divide into sections
F) to stop being with another person

Choose the correct meaning of *part* in each sentence.
Write the meaning on the line below the sentence.

1. I will **part** my hair in the middle to make braids.

   _____

2. Carrie got a large **part** in the play.

   _____

3. Campers **part** from their parents in the summer.

   _____

4. Elan used a knife to **part** the pizza.

   _____

5. The mechanic will call us when the **part** is in.

   _____

6. Mom told Ben to do his **part** to help with the chores.

   _____

Try This!

Look up the word **play** in the dictionary. Write three definitions for it.

Read for Meaning

Name _____

Read each sentence. Use the picture clue to help you figure out the meaning of the **boldfaced** word. Circle the correct meaning and write it on the line.

1. Tim was **exhausted** after playing four soccer games.

_____

tired   clean

2. As Lori bought more things, her savings **dwindled**.

_____

went down   went up

3. Gwen thought about all her **options** before making a decision.

_____

friends   choices

4. Sara wears a helmet so she does not **injure** herself if she falls.

_____

save   hurt

5. Ed will **exchange** his jeans for a larger size.

_____

sew   switch

6. Vin will take the motor apart so he can **explore** how it works.

_____

figure out   play

Try This!   What would you like to explore? Make a list.

What's in Space?

Name _____

Use the words in the Word Box to fill in the missing words in the facts below.

Word Box

star	moon	Earth	space	planets	universe	solar system

1. On a clear night, we can see the ⊙_ _ _.

2. We live on the planet called ⊙_ _ _ _.

3. There are eight other _ _ _ _ _ ⊙_.

4. The other planets are in _ _ _ _⊙.

5. All nine planets and the sun make up a
   _⊙_ _ _   _ _ _ _ _ _.

6. The solar system is one small part of the _ _ _ _ _⊙_ _.

7. Each ⊙_ _ _ in the sky may be a sun for another group of planets.

There are bodies in space that sometimes fall to Earth. To find out what they are called, write the circled letters in the order that they appear above.

_ _ _ _ _ _ _ _

Try This! Write two facts you know about the moon or the sun.

Water, Water Everywhere

Name _____

Water moves from **Earth** into the air and back to Earth over and over again. This is called the water **cycle**.

Rain can also be called **precipitation**. When rain falls, some of the water soaks into the ground. Other rainwater flows into rivers, lakes, or the **ocean**. The sun's heat causes the water to change from a liquid to a gas called water **vapor**. This change is called **evaporation**. Water vapor gathers to form clouds. As clouds become heavy with water, they form dark rain clouds. The heavy clouds cause water to fall. This is called **condensation**. Water falls from the clouds as rain, and the water cycle continues.

Find the **boldfaced** words in the puzzle. The words go across and down.

```
e  x  m  r  z  a  m  r  c  y  c  l  e  d  v  x
c  o  n  d  e  n  s  a  t  i  o  n  n  h  a  m
r  c  n  d  e  a  r  t  h  e  s  s  e  o  p  i
t  e  u  p  r  e  c  i  p  i  t  a  t  i  o  n
h  a  t  d  v  r  a  m  e  l  l  o  o  r  r  i
t  n  e  e  v  a  p  o  r  a  t  i  o  n  t  o
```

Try This! Write the **boldfaced** words above in alphabetical order.

FS-32502 Big Book of Basic Skills

Famous Americans

Using a code

Name _____

Complete each sentence. Use the code to help you.

A	B	C	D	E	F	G	H	I	J	K	L	M
1	2	3	4	5	6	7	8	9	10	11	12	13

N	O	P	Q	R	S	T	U	V	W	X	Y	Z
14	15	16	17	18	19	20	21	22	23	24	25	26

1. __ __ __ __ __ __ __ __ __ __ __ __ __ __ __ __
   7 5 15 18 7 5 23 1 19 8 9 14 7 20 15 14

   was the first president.

2. __ __ __ __ __ __. __ __ __ __ __ __ __
   19 21 19 1 14 2   1 14 20 8 15 14 25

   worked hard to give women the right to vote.

3. __ __ __ __ __ __ __ __ __ __ __ __ invented the light bulb.
   20 8 15 13 1 19   5 4 9 19 15 14

4. __ __ __ __ __ __ __ __ __ __ __ __ __ __ __ __ __ __ __
   1 12 5 24 1 14 4 5 18   7 18 1 8 1 13   2 5 12 12

   invented the telephone.

5. __ __ __ __ __ __ __ __ __ __ __ __ __ __ __
   2 5 14 10 1 13 9 14   6 18 1 14 11 12 9 14

   discovered electricity.

Try This!   Write the names of three other famous Americans.

© Frank Schaffer Publications, Inc.   〈184〉   FS-32502 Big Book of Basic Skills

VOCAB. DEV.

Just the Opposite

Name _____

Read each sentence. Use the picture clues to help you figure out the meaning of the **boldfaced** word. Circle the word that means the opposite and write it on the line.

1. Al was **disappointed** that he could not see the show.

_____

delighted   point

2. The 500-piece puzzle was **difficult** to put together.

_____

believe   easy

3. The magician will soon **reveal** what is inside the hat.

_____

cook   cover up

4. The old clock shows the **incorrect** time.

_____

right   morning

5. Raya's cat wanted to play in the **morning**.

_____

evening   bedtime

6. The young boy tried to **answer** a question.

_____

think   ask

Try This!   Write your own list of opposite word pairs.

Technology Tools

Context clue

Name _____

Read this story about technology tools. The **boldfaced** words may be new to you. Their meanings are given below the story. Write the word that matches each meaning.

No matter what kind of work you do as an adult, you will probably need to use a **computer**. You can enter words and numbers by typing them on a **keyboard**. A **monitor** will show your work as you type. It looks like a TV screen. When you are finished, the **printer** can be used to print out a **hard copy**. A **diskette** can be used to save your work. You can also add a **modem** to your computer. The modem helps you communicate with other people using your computer.

1. The tool used for typing words and numbers is a _____ .

2. The screen that shows your work is called a _____ .

3. The tool used to make a hard copy is a _____ .

4. The tool used for communicating with other people using the computer is called a _____ .

5. You save your work on a _____ .

6. The technology tool you need for now and for the future is a

    _____ .

7. Your printed pages are called a _____ .

Try This!   Write the **boldfaced** words in alphabetical order.

FS-32502 Big Book of Basic Skills

Vocabulary Checkup

Name _____

Finish the sentences. Fill in the bubbles to show your answers.

1. _____ are large hills made of sand.
   ○ Tides   ○ Dunes   ○ Waves

2. The _____ are what you need to follow a recipe.
   ○ refrigerator   ○ food processor   ○ ingredients

3. _____ grow underground on all types of plants.
   ○ Leaves   ○ Stems   ○ Roots

4. A baby bear is called a _____ .
   ○ cub   ○ pup   ○ calf

5. The day between Tuesday and Thursday is _____ .
   ○ Monday   ○ Wednesday   ○ Friday

6. Tall buildings are called _____ .
   ○ crosswalks   ○ skyscrapers   ○ metropolis

7. A six-sided figure is called a _____ .
   ○ pentagon   ○ hexagon   ○ octagon

8. The ordinal number between sixth and eighth is _____ .
   ○ fifth   ○ ninth   ○ seventh

Try This! Make a word search puzzle using your answers from above. Have a friend solve it.

FS-32502 Big Book of Basic Skills

Finish the Sentences

Name_____

Finish the sentences. Fill in the bubbles to show your answers.

1. The holiday that means "Fifth of May" is _____ .
   ○ Kwanzaa   ○ Christmas   ○ Cinco de Mayo

2. An object that is attracted to some metals is a _____ .
   ○ pole   ○ magnet   ○ negative

3. _____ means to use things over and over again.
   ○ Pollute   ○ Recycle   ○ Conserve

4. Books that are not true are called _____ .
   ○ fiction   ○ nonfiction   ○ history

5. _____ means choices.
   ○ Explores   ○ Options   ○ Dwindles

6. Earth is a _____ .
   ○ star   ○ planet   ○ universe

7. A word that means the opposite of delighted is _____ .
   ○ happy   ○ disappointed   ○ delicious

8. A _____ is a technology tool.
   ○ data   ○ computer   ○ communicate

Try This! Write your answers from above in alphabetical order.

CHAPTER 7

Reading Comprehension

Learning to read can sometimes be a frustrating experience for a child—and for the adults who are trying to help.

To help children learn to comprehend what they read, this chapter offers an interesting fact- or fiction-based story on each page. Each narrative has been written so that a child at a second-grade level can read it successfully. After each story, there are activities that will help children practice the following skills: locating the main idea, reading for details, putting events in order, following directions, determining the cause and the effect of an action, recognizing similarities and differences, analyzing characters, predicting outcomes, drawing conclusions, and much more. The carefully thought-out questions help a child learn to think, respond, create, imagine, and even do research to learn more about a subject.

You will be thrilled when the children completing these activities want to read more as they begin to better understand what they are reading. They will also learn to question and will develop higher-level thinking skills that are necessary in so many important aspects in life. Most of all, this chapter will help children recognize reading as an enjoyable way to spend their time.

The New Kid

Name _____

Every story has a **main idea**. The main idea is a sentence that tells what the whole story is about. Read this story about Maria. Answer the questions below.

It was Maria's first day at her new school. She missed her best friend, Sam. Maria looked at the kids on the playground. She wished she knew them. Maybe she would never have another friend, she thought. Then Maria felt a touch on her arm. "My name is Tiff," said a red-haired girl. "Do you want to play with me?"

1. Circle the best answer.

   This story is about   **Tiff.**   **Sam.**   **Maria.**

   The story happens at   **a park.**   **a school.**

   It was Maria's   **first**   **second**   day at this school.

2. Use a red crayon to underline the main idea of this story.

Try This!

- Draw a picture of the main idea of this story.
- Tell how you would have helped Maria if she had come to your school.

Arf!

Name _____

Casey loves dogs. He loves spotted dogs, tall dogs, and long dogs. He goes to the pet shop. He plays with the fluffy dogs and the short dogs. He draws skinny dogs on his napkin at dinner. Dogs are Casey's favorite kind of animal!

Underline the best answers.

1. This story is mainly about

    the kind of animal Casey loves.

    different kinds of dogs.

2. Casey loves

    all kinds of animals.

    all kinds of dogs.

3. Casey loves only spotted dogs, tall dogs, and long dogs.

    True   False

Try This! This story tells only one thing about Casey. Write two or three sentences that tell more about Casey.

A Cool Place

Name _____

Brad wants to go to a cool place. He wants to swim, dive, and splash. All Brad can think about is wearing his swimsuit in the cold blue water. He wants to play on his raft. Where does Brad want to go? He wants to go to the swimming pool, of course!

1. Put a √ next to the sentence that tells what the story is about.

   _____ **Brad wants to wear a swimsuit.**

   _____ **Brad is cool.**

   _____ **Brad wants to go to the swimming pool.**

2. There is one sentence in the paragraph that tells the main idea of the story. Write it here. _____
   _____.

3. Write two reasons why Brad wants to go to the pool.
   (A) _____
   (B) _____

Try This! Write about another place Brad could go. Write three reasons why the place you choose is *better* than the pool.

Pickles

Name _____

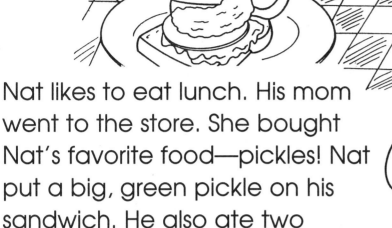

Nat likes to eat lunch. His mom went to the store. She bought Nat's favorite food—pickles! Nat put a big, green pickle on his sandwich. He also ate two pickles straight out of the jar. Nat loves pickles!

Word Box

apples	peas	pickles
candy	tickles	good
bad	pocket	mouth
jar	Nate	Nat

Use the words in the Word Box to answer the questions.

1. Who is this story about? _____.

2. What does Nat love? _____

3. Draw a green line under the main idea in the story.

Try This!

- Write a new title for this story.
- Write a sentence about something you love.

A Backyard Zoo

Name _____

My name is Kim. I want to go to the zoo. There are animals at the zoo. Big animals and little animals live there. But my mom says she is busy. She cannot take me to the zoo. My dog, Ellie, and I are sad. We decide to go outside.

Ellie lies in the grass. I lie down by her. Wow! A blue butterfly flies past my nose. A brown cricket crawls on my hand. I look at a tan snail on a gray rock. A little red ladybug lands on Ellie. "Mom!" I yell. "We have a zoo in our backyard!"

Answer the questions below about the details in the story.

1. Where does Kim want to go? _____

_____

2. Why can't Kim's mom go to the zoo? _____

_____

3. What color is the butterfly? _____

4. Where did Kim see the brown cricket?_____

_____

Try This!

- Draw a picture of Kim in her backyard "zoo."
- List two other animals you might find in your backyard. Add them to the picture you drew of Kim.

FS-32502 Big Book of Basic Skills

Summer Vacation

Name _____

Sandie and Taylor are out of school for the summer. The two friends make a list of fun things they want to do. Sandie wants to jump rope and go to the pool. Taylor wants to dig for dinosaur bones and ride her bike. Sandie and Taylor both want to eat pizza and stay up late. The girls will have so much fun!

1. Draw a line from each girl's picture to the things she wants to do.

Sandie

ride a bike

go to the pool

eat pizza

dig for dinosaur bones

stay up late

jump rope

Taylor

2. How many things does Sandie want to do? _____

3. Circle the thing Taylor and Sandie both want to do.

jump rope   **stay up late**   **ride a bike**

Try This!

Plan your own summer vacation. Use a calendar to help you decide what to do and when to do it.

FS-32502 Big Book of Basic Skills

New Bikes

Name _____

Mary and Lori got new bikes. Lori picked a blue bike with a red seat and yellow handlebars. Mary chose a purple bike with a pink seat and yellow handlebars. Mary and Lori rode to school on their bikes. They parked them in the bike rack. The two girls love their new bikes!

Fill in the blanks with the best answers.

1. What color is the seat on Mary's bike?_____

2. Mary and Lori park their bikes in the _____ at school.

3. What is the one thing that is the same color on both of the new bikes? _____

Circle the best answers.

4. Who has the blue bike?   **Mary**   **Lori**

5. Mary and Lori walk their bikes to school.   **True**   **False**

Write a short story in which Mary and Lori use their bikes to solve a problem.

196

Teddy Bear's Morning

Name _____

Teddy Bear woke up. The sun was shining in his window. "Hello, new day!" he said. It was time to get up. He needed to find his clothes.

Teddy found his blue shorts under his bed. He put them on. Teddy put on his green shirt. Teddy's shoes were in the dog's bed. Teddy put on his shoes.

Next, Teddy Bear brushed his teeth. He washed his face and combed his hair. Now Teddy was hungry. Mama Bear called him to breakfast. After he ate, Teddy cleaned his room. Teddy Bear had a busy morning.

Put the sentences below in order.
Write a number in front of each one.

_____ Mama Bear called Teddy to breakfast.

_____ Teddy got dressed.

_____ Teddy woke up.

_____ Teddy brushed his teeth.

_____ Teddy cleaned his room.

Try This!

- What could Teddy do to make it easier to get dressed?
- Make a list of the things you do after you wake up in the morning.

Bubbling Over

Name _____

Making a volcano is fun! First, use paste to stick half of an empty eggshell on a piece of cardboard. Make sure the open part is at the top. Next, pile some dirt and sand around the eggshell. This makes it look like a real volcano. Put some red food coloring and baking soda into the eggshell. Then pour a little bit of vinegar into the eggshell. If nothing happens, add more vinegar. Watch your volcano "erupt." Add more baking soda and vinegar if you want it to erupt again.

1. If you want to make your own volcano, first you should

    _____.

2. Put a **2** next to the second thing you need to do. Put a **3** next to the third thing you need to do. Put a **4** next to the fourth thing you need to do.

    _____ Put red food coloring and baking soda into the eggshell.

    _____ Pour vinegar into the eggshell.

    _____ Pile dirt and sand around the eggshell.

Try This! Think of something you know how to do really well. Write down the steps that tell how to do it. Or draw pictures that show how to do it.

〈198〉 FS-32502 Big Book of Basic Skills

Rocky's Party

Name _____

Rocky Coyote's friends gave him a party. Rosie Bird gave Rocky balloons. Ben Bunny took pretty rocks to the party. Zach Zebra took forks. Hilda Hamster made pizza. Tilly Tiger took her camera. Barney Bat gave Rocky a radio. They all had fun.

1. In the picture above, color Rocky Coyote brown.

2. Color purple what Rosie Bird took to the party.

3. Color what Zach Zebra took to the party blue.

4. Draw a pink circle around what Ben Bunny gave Rocky.

5. Draw an X on the friend who made pizza.

6. Color the food red.

7. Draw a △ around what Tilly Tiger took.

8. Draw a yellow circle around what Barney Bat gave Rocky.

Try This!

- Draw what you would have brought to this party.
- Choose one of the friends in the story. Write four sentences telling what this friend is like.

Killer Whales

Name _____

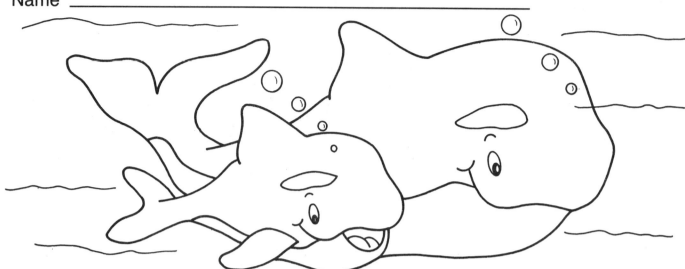

Killer whales are big animals. They have many sharp teeth, but they are not mean to people. These whales are black and white. They often travel in groups of two or more. A killer whale can swim up to 35 miles per hour. Killer whales like to eat large fish. Would you like to see a killer whale?

_____

Read and follow the directions carefully.

1. Underline something a killer whale eats.

2. This paragraph is about _____ _____.

3. Circle the two words you wrote above wherever you see them on this page.

4. The paragraph above ends with a question. Write your answer to that question here. _____

5. Draw a blue **X** on top of a word in the paragraph that tells what killer whales are *not*.

Try This! Give three good reasons why you would or would not like to see a killer whale. Write your reasons with a black crayon.

FS-32502 Big Book of Basic Skills

Pancakes for Dinner

Name _____

Sometimes my mom cooks pancakes for dinner. She reads the box. I help add the milk. Mom cracks the eggs. She lets me stir the batter. The batter is hard to stir. It gets thick. The pan is hot. The pancakes sizzle. My mom can flip the pancakes high in the air. I can have the big pancake. I love pancakes for dinner!

1. Color the pancake box yellow.

2. Draw a red circle around the hot pan.

3. Draw a green line from the milk carton to the bowl.

4. Put a line of orange ●●●●●● from the bowl to the pan.

5. Color the boy's shoes purple.

Try This! Draw a picture of the boy helping his dad wash the dishes.

Plants, Please!

Name _____

Shannon plants a carrot seed and a radish seed. She plants the carrot seed in good soil. She waters it and puts it in a sunny spot. Soon, the carrot seed grows into a plant. Shannon plants her radish seed in sand. She puts it in a dark room. She does not give the radish seed any water. The radish seed never grows into a plant! Shannon now knows what a plant needs to grow. Do you?

---

1. Shannon's carrot seed grew into a plant because _____
   _____.

2. Shannon planted her radish seed in sand, put it in a dark place, and did not water it. As a result, it_____.

3. What are three things that help a plant grow?

   _____   _____   _____

Try This! Plant a seed in a cup. See how long it takes to sprout.

FS-32502 Big Book of Basic Skills

What Happened?

Name _____

Nick liked walking. He walked in the woods near his home. It started raining. The ground got all wet. Nick stepped in a puddle. He looked down and saw that his shoes were muddy. Nick knew he would be in trouble. His shoes were brand new! Nick ran home and put them in the washing machine. He wanted to wash them before his mom got home.

Circle the words that make each sentence true.

1. Nick's shoes got muddy because

   he stepped in a puddle.   **they were new.**   **he liked walking.**

2. Nick ran home and

   read his favorite book.   **washed his shoes.**

3. Why was the ground wet? _____

4. Nick wanted to wash his shoes before _____

   _____.

Try This! Read a paragraph in your favorite book. Find something that happened. Draw a picture of what caused it to happen.

‹203›   FS-32502 Big Book of Basic Skills

Get Crafty!

Name _____

You and an adult can make something that is like clay. Put 2 cups of starch in a pot. Add 2 cups of salt. Also add 1½ cups of water. Stir over low heat using a wooden spoon. The mixture will turn into a ball. Let it cool. Use it to make beads, napkin rings, and other fun things. You may add food coloring to make different colors of clay. Or you can paint what you make after it dries. Have fun!

Circle or write the best answers.

1. After you heat and stir the mixture of salt, starch, and water,

   it will get cold.   **it will turn into a ball.**   **it will smell bad.**

2. If you add food coloring, the clay will _____

   _____.

3. You can also make your clay colorful by_____

   _____

Try This! Draw pictures showing how to make the clay above. Be sure to make a picture for each step.

FS-32502 Big Book of Basic Skills

Picnic at the Park

Name _____

Four friends had a picnic at the park. Jason's mother brought him in her car. He brought his new puppy. Amber rode her bike. Her cat followed her. Seth walked. He brought his

hamster in his shirt pocket. Kyle walked, and he brought his parrot. Jason brought apples, pears, and peaches. Seth brought pretzels, granola bars, and cheese. Amber brought hot dogs and peanut butter sandwiches. Kyle brought juice. The four friends ate and had a great time.

Circle the correct answers to the questions below.

1. _____ and _____ used wheels to come to the party.

   Jason   **Kyle**   **Amber**   **Seth**

2. The _____ was brought by Seth.

   fruit   **juice**   **cheese**   **milk**

3. The pets at the picnic included a _____ and a _____ .

   hamster   **cat**   **pig**   **horse**

4. Look at the foods in the story. Write what foods you would have eaten at the picnic. _____

   _____

Try This!   Draw a picture of a healthy meal you would like to eat.

Fish or Mammal?

Name _____

Fish and mammals are two kinds of animals. Fish lay eggs. After most baby fish hatch, they spend all their lives in the water. They have no hair. They use gills to breathe. Goldfish are a kind of fish.

Mammals have hair. They use lungs to breathe. Most mammal babies are born live. Some mammals live on land. Other mammals live part of their lives on land and part in the water. A whale is a mammal.

Fill in the blanks with the best answers.

1. What kind of animal uses gills? _____

2. Most fish spend all their lives _____.

3. Write the name of a mammal that lives on land.

   _____

4. Write the name of a mammal that lives in the water.

   _____

Try This! Find out more about mammals or fish at the library. Choose an animal. Make a small book about the animal. Use your book to help your friends learn about the animal.

The Birthday

Name _____

Four children sat in a dark room. "Shh! Be quiet!" whispered Scott. The door opened. A light came on. "Surprise! Happy Birthday!" shouted the four friends. Kate jumped. She put her hands over her eyes. Then she laughed. Kate began to open her gifts. Christy smiled when Kate opened the box she had brought. It was a funny book. Tyler is Kate's little brother. He ran to his room to cry. No one had brought him a gift. Aaron sat with Tyler. Aaron said, "You will get presents on your birthday." Aaron wiped Tyler's tears.

happy	mad	sad	unhappy
glad	surprised	bossy	pleased
helpful	nice	kind	unkind

Use words from the box to tell about each person in the story.

1. Kate _____

2. Tyler _____

3. Aaron _____

4. Scott _____

5. Christy _____

Try This! Choose a word from the box. Write a sentence using that word.

At the Beach

Character analys[...]

Name _____

Carla's class went on a field trip to the beach. Max pushed Jan out of the way. He wanted to get off the bus first. But Julie told him, "Max, don't push anyone else or I'll tell the teacher!" On the beach, Carla found a pretty pink

shell. She gave it to Gaby, the new girl in the class. Gaby smiled but didn't say anything. When Carla asked Gaby, "Do you like it?" Gaby nodded and ran back to the bus. After awhile, Carla's teacher said, "Okay class, let's go. I have a treat for everyone!"

Circle the word that best tells about each person in the story.

1. Carla is a **silly   kind   sad**   girl.

2. Gaby seems to be   **angry.   happy.   shy.**

3. When Max pushed Jan, he was being   **mean.   mad.   sweet.**

4. A good word to describe Julie is   **funny.   bossy.   shy.**

Try This!

Which character from this story would you choose to be your friend? Write three or four reasons telling why you would choose this person.

FS-32502 Big Book of Basic Skills

Four Frog Friends

Name _____

Four frog friends sat on a rock. They were hungry for bugs. They had not eaten since lunch. There were no bugs flying around them. "My mom told me to sit still and bugs will come," said Fanny Frog. "I believe her." She looked left and right. She would be ready when they came. "If they do, you won't catch any!" shouted Frankie Frog. He frowned at Fanny. Three bugs began to fly close. "I know I will catch one of those! I am sure of it," said Frieda. She caught one and smiled. "Gulp." "Don't worry, Fanny," said Farah. "I will help you get a bug." The frogs waited some more.

Draw a line from each frog to the word that tells about it.

Frankie	Frieda	Fanny	Farah

helpful	trusting	mean	certain

Try This! Draw pictures of yourself and four friends. Write a word under each friend's picture that tells about him or her.

FS-32502 Big Book of Basic Skills

Which Season?

Name _____

What a beautiful day! The air is cool and crisp. The squirrels are looking for nuts. There are no clouds in the sky. Look at the leaves! They are red, yellow, orange, and brown. People are wearing sweaters and pants. The sun is shining.

Think about the story when you answer these questions.

1. What do you think will happen to the leaves in a month or two?

   _____

2. The season you read about in this paragraph is called
   _____ . The next season after that will be
   _____.

3. What will people be wearing in the next season? _____

   _____

   Why? _____

Try This! Write a paragraph about summer. Tell about the weather, animals, and plants. Also tell what people are wearing.

The Gift

Name _____

It was summer. Katelyn and Tommy were glad. Today, Mom said they could do something special. She gave them each a small sack. "Wow!" they said. "What is this?" Mom smiled. "Look inside," she said. They quickly tore open their bags.  "Are these little rocks?" cried Tommy. "No," said Mom. "What are they?" asked Katelyn. Inside the bag, they saw round, tan things. There was a drawing of a carrot on one bag. There was a drawing of a green bean on the other bag.

---

1. Circle the answer that tells what you think happened next.

   Mom gave them magic stones.

   Mom gave them carrot and bean seeds.

"You have carrot seeds, Tommy. And you have bean seeds, Katelyn," said Mom. "Plant them and help them grow."

---

2. Circle the answer that tells what you think happened next.

   Katelyn and Tommy planted the seeds.

   Katelyn and Tommy dropped the seeds and went inside.

3. Circle the answer that tells what you think happened later.

   Later, the plants started to grow.

   Later, a carrot tree grew and the kids climbed it.

Try This!

Plant some seeds. Put them in the sun. Water them. Keep a journal telling about what happens each day.

Peep!

Name _____

Mockingbirds are busy! One lives in a tree near my door. It always has something to do. First, it builds a nest. Then, it lays its eggs. After some time passes, I hear the new babies peeping. The mother mockingbird flies away soon after they hatch. I wonder why it does that! It seems to be looking for something.

Circle or write the best answers.

1. Why does the mother bird leave the nest so soon after its babies hatch? _____

2. After the babies hatch, they will probably

   peep for food.   **fly away.**   **take a bath.**

3. What do you think will happen to the baby mockingbirds after a few weeks? _____

_____

Try This! What do you think it would be like to be a mother mockingbird? Would you like it? Why or why not?

FS-32502 Big Book of Basic Skills

Ziggy and Zoey

Name _____

Ziggy and Zoey were skating fast on the playground. Ziggy fell. He came into the classroom crying. "I need some bandages," he said to his teacher, Mrs. Booker. She helped him clean up. "A helmet would help keep you safe, Ziggy," said Mrs. Booker. "You should also wear pads on your knees and elbows." "I sure do not want to get hurt again," said Ziggy. "It's no fun. Zoey fell, but she did not get hurt. She wears a helmet and pads."

Circle the answers you think are correct.

1. Ziggy and Zoey were playing at **school.** **home.**

2. Zoey wore a helmet and knee pads. **True** **False**

3. Ziggy was careful when he skated. **True** **False**

4. Ziggy will wear a helmet and pads next time. **True** **False**

5. Mrs. Booker is a **bossy** **helpful** person.

Try This! What do you think happened to Ziggy on the playground? Draw a picture of what you think Ziggy will look like in his safety gear.

Busy Leaf-cutter Ants

Name _____

Leaf-cutter ants work hard. The queen lays eggs. Some of her worker ants take care of the eggs and young ants. Other ants strip leaves from plants. They bring the parts back to the ant mound. Most of the ants use the leaf parts to help grow fungus they eat. Not one worker ant rests!

Use the paragraph to help you answer the questions.

1. Why do the ants work so hard? _____

_____

2. What might happen to the eggs if the worker ants do not care for them? _____

_____

Circle the best answers.

3. Ants cut up plant leaves to

    help grow a fungus.   **build a house.**   **have a snack.**

4. The ants make the fungus because

    it looks pretty.   **they use it for food.**

Try This! Leaf-cutter ants come in many different sizes. Pretend you are the smallest leaf-cutter ant. Write a letter to an ant friend in another ant mound telling about your life.

214

It's a Mystery!

Name _____

Dad was happy. He sang a happy song. It was a warm day. There were lots of things to eat. Dad pulled something from the ground. It wiggled, but he held on. Dad flew to find Mom. She was sitting on two eggs. Dad gave the food to Mom for breakfast. She ate it quickly. She felt something move under her. The eggs were cracking. She heard two peeps. She looked and saw two fuzzy heads! Dad flew off to find more food. Mom and the babies would want food. Mom was happy. She began to sing.

1. Color blue the picture that shows what kind of animals are in the story.

2. Use a red crayon to circle the number of babies Mom and Dad have in the nest.

3. With a brown crayon, color the food that Dad brought Mom.

4. Circle the time of year this story takes place.

Spring   **Winter**

Try This!

- Draw a picture to show this family.
- Make up a new three-word title for this story.

Going for a Ride

Alike and
different

Name _____

Some people drive cars to
work. Other people ride a
bus. A car has wheels. A bus
has wheels, too. But some
buses have more wheels
than cars. A bus has a
motor. So does a car. A car
and a bus both have
windows. But a bus has more
windows than a car. A bus can carry more people than a
car. A bus has headlights to turn on when it gets dark. So
does a car. A bus is much bigger than a car. Cars have seat
belts. Most buses do not. Which would you rather ride in?

1. Circle everything that cars and buses have.

   seat belts   wheels   motors   steps   headlights

2. Tell about one more thing that is the same about cars and
   buses. _____

3. Write three ways that a bus and a car are different.

   _____

   _____

   _____

Try This!

Pretend you are going on a long trip. Would you rather
take a bus or a car? Draw a picture of the bus or car
that would be great for your trip. Write a few sentences
about the bus or car.

216

Scooter and Spot

Name _____

Scooter and Spot are friends. Some things they do alike. Some things they do differently. Spot and Scooter like to eat and take naps. Spot likes baths and running with a ball in his mouth. Scooter hates baths. Scooter never runs with a ball in her mouth. Both friends have long tails, gray fur, and four feet. Scooter and Spot each have teeth. Scooter says "Meow!" Spot barks.

Put a √ to show how the friends are alike and different.

	Scooter	Spot
1. Takes naps		
2. Plays with balls		
3. Likes to take baths		
4. Says "Meow!"		
5. Has four feet		

Try This!

Draw a picture of yourself and a friend. Show how you are the same. Make a list of six ways you and your friend are different.

Swimmers

Alike and differer

Name _____

A dolphin is like a shark in some ways. But a dolphin is different from a shark in other ways. Dolphins and sharks both swim. A dolphin is a mammal. A shark is a fish. Both have fins. A shark uses gills to breathe. A dolphin has lungs for breathing. Sharks have teeth, and so do dolphins. Dolphins live in family groups. Sharks mainly live alone. Would you rather be a dolphin or a shark?

Fill in the blanks with the best answers.

1. Dolphins are like sharks in some ways. They both_____
   _____. They both _____.
   They both _____.

2. Draw lines from each animal to the things that make it different from the other animal.

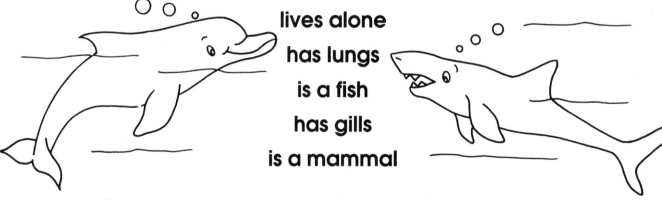

lives alone

has lungs

is a fish

has gills

is a mammal

Try This! Pretend you have to sell a dolphin and a shark. Make one poster for each animal. It should tell people about the animals. Be sure to write only good things about the animals. Which would be easier to sell? Why?

FS-32502 Big Book of Basic Skil

Butterflies and Moths

Name _____

Can you tell a butterfly from a moth? They both have eyes, legs, wings, heads, and bodies. If you know how, though, you can tell them apart! When butterflies rest, they usually hold their wings up. Most moths hold their wings flat when resting. Most butterflies fly in the daytime. Moths usually fly at night. You can see moths around lights at night. Most butterflies are brightly colored. Moths are usually shades of brown. Now you can tell a butterfly from a moth, too!

1. Circle the things butterflies and moths both have.

   wings   wheels   eyes   bright colors

2. Put a √ in front of each butterfly fact.

   _____ a. It holds its wings up when resting.

   _____ b. It is usually a shade of brown.

   _____ c. It will fly around lights at night.

   _____ d. It flies in the daytime.

   _____ e. It holds its wings flat when it rests.

   _____ f. It usually has bright colors.

Try This!   Draw a picture of your favorite butterfly.

CHAPTER 8

Choral Reading

Choral reading fosters a love of language and an appreciation for poetry. Children enjoy reading poems aloud expressively, and learn how language is used in the process. This type of reading also helps children develop reading and speaking skills, learn to cooperate, and extend their vocabularies. Everyone gains from participating in choral reading. Students who have strong verbal skills have the perfect opportunity to use them, while students who are less verbal, or shy, can enjoy group participation.

This chapter features poems of varying lengths. Begin with the short poems and move on to the longer ones as your students' skills with choral reading develop. Start by reading a poem aloud to your students, modeling the way you want them to read it. Discuss the mood that a poem evokes. Help the children see how the author's choice of words communicates feelings or experiences. You will also want to help your students feel the beat and rhythm of a selection.

Suggestions for assigning parts are included with the poems. Have the entire group learn a new poem together in unison first. Then assign the parts and direct the students as they read their assigned parts. Have the students stand in an arrangement that is appropriate for the selection. For some poems, the students can stand in two groups. For other poems, a large group of students can stand behind individual speakers who are standing in a row (speaker 1, speaker 2, and so on).

Teaching tips for some of the public domain poems found in this book are provided below. Be sure to try out your own ideas and those of your students. Experiment and enjoy!

If You Should Meet a Crocodile—Page 222
Although this is a humorous rhyme, encourage your students to recite their lines with mock seriousness, as if the warning were real. Explain to your students that the word *whene'er* is often used in poetry to replace the word *whenever*. Help your students practice saying *whene'er*, pronouncing it with only two syllables.

One Misty, Moisty Morning—Page 223
Cloth-ed is pronounced with two syllables to keep the rhythm of the verse.

Go to Bed Early—Page 224
Have the speakers step forward and act out their lines when reciting them. Speaker 1 stretches arms to wake up with a happy smile; Speaker 2 folds hands across chest, stomps foot, frowns; Speaker 3 throws an imaginary ball; Speaker 4 looks listless and tired with slouched posture and droopy face; Speaker 5 shows off biceps like a body builder; Speaker 6 puts chin in hands, sad-looking face; Speaker 7 stands up tall and proud; Speaker 8 slouches and shrinks smaller.

Harvest Song—Page 225
Tell your students that a *bough* is a tree branch.

An Autumn Morning—Page 228
Provide pictures of the different kinds of trees mentioned (oak, maple, elm, beech, chestnut) if possible. If desired, have five groups of students make child-size butcher paper trees that match the lines in the poem. Have each speaker hold up the matching tree when saying his or her lines.

The Leaves—Page 230
Select a few volunteers to act the part of the leaves by dancing, whirling, and so on while the rest of the class recites the poem.

The New Year—Page 231
Discuss the meaning of the poem with your students. Together, make a class list of all the things that the poem says the new year will bring (good wishes, a few cares, work, play, warm days, cold days, bright days, dull weather, gay seasons). Review the list with your students and ask them if they agree that the new year will bring each item listed. Explain to the students that the word *ne'er* in the last line is a shortened form of *never*.

How Many?—Page 233
Explain to your students that the word *runn'th* is a shortened form of the word *runneth*. Encourage the speakers to ask their questions with animation and curiosity. The answers can be given in a scholarly manner.

Winter and Spring—Page 234
As students recite this poem, the mood should gradually change from quiet and sad in the first two stanzas to increasing animation and excitement in the third and fourth stanzas. The fifth stanza should be read with lively exuberance.

The Wind—Page 236
The chorus stanzas (read by *All*) can be said in low tones with a melodramatic style.

The Railroad Cars Are Coming—Page 238
Encourage your students to read the poem with enthusiasm. Students can begin reading at a slow to moderate pace and then pick up speed through the second half of the poem.

Ducks' Ditty—Page 240
This delightful poem is from *The Wind in the Willows*. To ensure your students' full enjoyment of it, be sure to discuss the meanings of the following words: *rushes, dabbling, larder, swifts*. (Encourage students to use the context of the poem to try to determine the word meanings. Give help as needed.)

A Child's Song—Page 241
This poem has been adapted from "A Boy's Song" by James Hogg. Explain to your students that *lea* is another word for *meadow* and that *o'er* is a shortened form of the word *over*.

Grasshopper Green—Page 242
For a performance, have the speakers make and hold up the following props: Speaker 1—a picture of a grasshopper; Speaker 2—a picture of green trousers, jacket, and cap; Speaker 3—a picture of the sun; Speaker 4—a picture of a little house; Speaker 5—a picture of a spider; Speaker 6—a picture of two children.

Hiawatha's Brothers by Henry Wadsworth Longfellow—Page 245
Be sure to have the students pause for a moment between the first and second stanzas.

Over in the Meadow—Pages 246–247
Have the students pause briefly at the end of each stanza and act out what the animals in the stanza are doing.

The Hayloft—Page 248
Have the students read the first two stanzas in quiet, subdued voices. The last two stanzas should be read with joyful enthusiasm. Ask students to use context clues to discover the meaning of the word *scythes*. Give help as needed.

Beware!

Name _____

If You Should Meet a Crocodile

Author Unknown

Group 1: **If you should meet a crocodile,**
Don't take a stick and poke him;

Group 2: **Ignore the welcome in his smile,**
Be careful not to stroke him.

Group 3: **For as he sleeps upon the Nile,**
He thinner gets and thinner;

All: **And whene'er you meet a crocodile**
He's ready for his dinner.

Try This!

Complete the sentence with the name of another animal and a warning. Then draw a picture to illustrate your sentence.

If you should meet a _____, don'

_____

Polite Words

Name _____

One Misty, Moisty Morning

Anonymous

All: **One misty, moisty morning,**
When cloudy was the weather,
(Look up to the sky.)

Group 1:   **I chanced to meet an old man,**
Clothed all in leather.
(Shake hands with a pretend person.)

Group 2:   **He began to compliment**
And I began to grin.
(Smile.)

All: **How do you do?**
And how do you do?
And how do you do again?
(Bow.)

Try This!

Manners are rules that tell polite ways to treat people. Make a list of good manners on the back of this page. Then make a book about good manners. Write and illustrate one rule on each page.

Good Night

Name _____

Go to Bed Early

Traditional

All:	**Go to bed early—**
Speaker 1:	**Wake up with joy,**
All:	**Go to bed late—**
Speaker 2:	**Cross girl or boy.**
All:	**Go to bed early—**
Speaker 3:	**Ready for play,**
All:	**Go to bed late—**
Speaker 4:	**Moping all day.**
All:	**Go to bed early—**
Speaker 5:	**No pains or ills,**
All:	**Go to bed late—**
Speaker 6:	**Doctors and pills.**
All:	**Go to bed early—**
Speaker 7:	**Grow very tall,**
All:	**Go to bed late**
Speaker 8:	**Stay very small.**

Try This!

Write pairs of rhyming words from this poem.

_____ _____ _____

_____ _____ _____

224

FS-32502 Big Book of Basic Sk

Harvest Home

Name _____

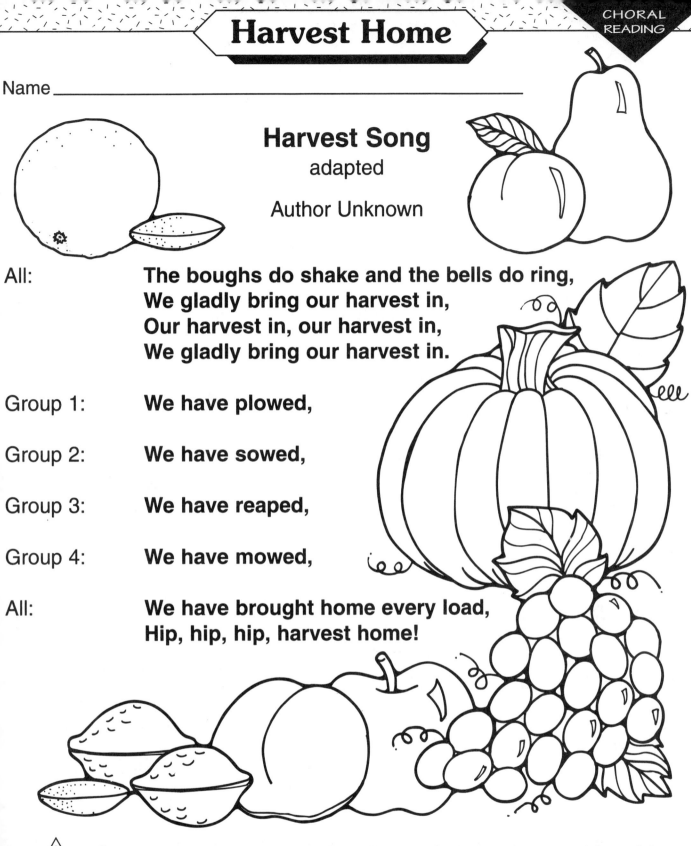

Harvest Song

adapted

Author Unknown

All: The boughs do shake and the bells do ring,
We gladly bring our harvest in,
Our harvest in, our harvest in,
We gladly bring our harvest in.

Group 1: We have plowed,

Group 2: We have sowed,

Group 3: We have reaped,

Group 4: We have mowed,

All: We have brought home every load,
Hip, hip, hip, harvest home!

Try This! Paint life-size pictures of different fruits and vegetables. After the paint dries, cut them out. On another sheet of paper, paint a picture of a basket. Arrange your cutouts to look like fruits and vegetables in the basket. Then glue them in place.

FS-32502 Big Book of Basic Skills

Yum, Yum, Yum

Name _____

Popcorn

Anonymous

Group 1:   **Dance, little corn seeds,**
            Hop, hop, hop!
            (Jump up with both feet together.)

Group 2:   **Soon we shall hear you**
            Pop, pop, pop!
            (Close fists, stretch hands up, open fists.)

Group 1:   **Keep on dancing**
            Please do not stop
            (Jump up with both feet together.)

Group 2:   **Till our pan is full**
            To the top, top, top!
            (Stretch hands up high.)

Try This!   Write about times when you like to eat popcorn.

_____

_____

_____

FS-32502 Big Book of Basic Skills

Name _____

The Land of Nod

Robert Louis Stevenson

Group 1: **From breakfast on all through the day**
At home among my friends I stay;

Group 2: **But every night I go abroad**
Afar into the land of Nod.

Group 1: **All by myself I have to go,**
With none to tell me what to do

Group 2: **All alone beside the streams**
And up the mountain-side of dreams.

Try This!

Write a sentence telling something you like to do when you are with your friends.

_____

_____

Write a sentence telling something you like to do when you are alone.

_____

_____

Rich Colors

Name _____

An Autumn Morning

Author Unknown

All:
> It seems like a dream
> In the garden today;
> The trees, once so green,
> With rich colors are gay.

Speaker 1:
> The oak is aglow
> With a warm, crimson blush;

Speaker 2:
> The maple leaves show
> A deep purple flush.

Speaker 3:
> The elm tree with bold
> Yellow patches is bright,

Speaker 4:
> And with pale gleaming gold
> The beech seems alight.

Speaker 5:
> The big chestnut trees
> Are all russet and brown,

Speaker 6:
> And everywhere leaves
> One by one flutter down.

All:
> And all the leaves seem
> To be dressed up so gay,
> That it seems like a dream
> In the garden today.

Try This! Use crayons to draw a picture of trees in autumn. Show trees with red leaves, purple leaves, yellow leaves, brown leaves, and orange leaves.

FS-32502 Big Book of Basic Skills

Name _____

A Farmer Went Trotting

Traditional

Speaker 1: **A farmer went trotting upon his gray mare;**

All: **Bumpety, bumpety, bump!**

Speaker 2: **With his daughter behind him, so rosy and fair;**

All: **Lumpety, lumpety, lump!**

Speaker 3: **A raven cried, "Croak!" and they all tumbled down;**

All: **Bumpety, bumpety, bump!**

Speaker 4: **The mare broke her knees, and the farmer his crown;**

All: **Lumpety, lumpety, lump!**

Speaker 5: **The mischievous raven flew laughing away;**

All: **Bumpety, bumpety, bump!**

Speaker 6: **And said he would serve them the same the next day;**

All: **Lumpety, lumpety, lump!**

Try This!

Draw comic-strip pictures that tell this story. Use word bubbles to show what the characters might have said.

Leaf Dance

Name _____

The Leaves

Author Unknown

Group 1: **The leaves had a wonderful frolic,**
They danced to the wind's loud song,

Group 2: **They whirled, and they floated, and scampered,**
They circled and flew along.

Group 3: **The moon saw the little leaves dancing,**
Each looked like a small brown bird.

Group 4: **The man in the moon smiled and listened,**
And this is the song he heard:

All: **The North Wind is calling, is calling,**
And we must whirl round and round,
And then when our dancing is ended
We'll make a warm quilt for the ground.

Try This! Make a leafy headband. Cut a strip of construction paper long enough to go around your head. Tape the ends together. Glue autumn leaves onto the headband. Or, cut orange, red, yellow, and brown leaves from paper and glue them to the headband. Wear the headband when you say the poem.

FS-32502 Big Book of Basic Skills

Happy New Year

Name _____

The New Year

Author Unknown

All:
Oh! I'm the New Year,
Come look at my wares;
I've wishes all good
And just a few cares.

Group 1:
Oh! What will you have?
Come, buy, young and old;
I've work and I've play,
I've days warm and cold.

Group 2:
Oh! What will you have?
There's no time to lose,
Bright days or dull weather,
I know which you'll choose.

Group 3:
And for little children
I've seasons so gay,
And each has a portion
Of work and of play.

All:
So come, young and old,
And buy from my pack,
And be sure with each purchase
Good luck you'll ne'er lack.

Try This! Make a list of three things you want to do in the new year.
Then list three things you want to learn in the new year.

  231 FS-32502 Big Book of Basic Skills

Winter Thoughts

Name _____

Thoughts for a Cold Day

Author Unknown

Group 1:   **A little bit of blowing,**

Group 2:   **A little bit of snow,**

Group 1:   **A little bit of growing,**

Group 2:   **And crocuses will show;**

Group 1:   **On every twig that's lonely**
            A new green leaf will spring;

Group 2:   **On every patient tree-top**
            A thrush will stop and sing.

Try This!   Draw signs of winter and signs of spring in the boxes below.

Winter Signs	Spring Signs

Name _____

How Many?

Christina Rossetti

Speaker 1:	**How many seconds in a minute?**
All:	**Sixty and no more in it.**
Speaker 2:	**How many minutes in an hour?**
All:	**Sixty for sun and shower.**
Speaker 3:	**How many hours in a day?**
All:	**Twenty-four for work and play.**
Speaker 4:	**How many days in a week?**
All:	**Seven both to hear and speak.**
Speaker 5:	**How many weeks in a month?**
All:	**Four, as the swift moon runn'th.**
Speaker 6:	**How many months in a year?**
All:	**Twelve the almanac makes clear.**
Speaker 7:	**How many years in an age?**
All:	**One hundred says the sage.**
Speaker 8:	**How many ages in time?**
All:	**No one knows the rhyme.**

Try This! List two things that take about one minute to do, two things that take about one hour to do, and two things that take about one day to do.

FS-32502 Big Book of Basic Skills

Spring Song

Winter and Spring

Author Unknown

Group 1:   **But a little while ago**
All the ground was white with snow;

Group 2:   **Trees and shrubs were dry and bare,**
Not a sign of life was there;

Group 1:   **Now the buds and leaves are seen,**
Now the fields are fresh and green,

Group 2:   **Pretty birds are on the wing,**
With a merry song they sing!

All: **There's new life in everything!**
How I love the pleasant spring!

Try This!   Write about your favorite season. Tell which season is your favorite and why. Tell what you like to do during that season.

_____

_____

_____

_____

Name _____

Open Sesame

Author Unknown

Speaker 1:   **Oh, for a book and a shady nook**
             Either in-a-door or out,

Speaker 2:   **With the green leaves whispering overhead**
             Or the street cry all about,

Speaker 3:   **Where I may read all at my ease,**
             Both of the new and old;

All: **For a jolly good book whereon to look**
             Is better to me than gold.

Try This!   Finish the sentences below.

Two of my favorite books are

_____

_____

My favorite place to read is

_____

_____

A Windy Day

Name _____

The Wind

Robert Louis Stevenson

Speaker 1:   **I saw you toss the kites on high
And blow the birds about the sky;**

Speaker 2:   **And all around I heard you pass,
Like ladies' skirts across the grass—**

All: **O wind, a-blowing all day long,
O wind, that sings so loud a song!**

Speaker 3:   **I saw the different things you did,
But always you yourself you hid.**

Speaker 4:   **I felt you push, I heard you call,
I could not see yourself at all—**

All: **O wind, a-blowing all day long,
O wind, that sings so loud a song!**

Speaker 5:   **O you that are so strong and cold,
O blower are you young or old?**

Speaker 6:   **Are you a beast of field and tree
Or just a stronger child than me?**

All: **O wind, a-blowing all day long,
O wind, that sings so loud a song!**

Try This! Imagine that you are the wind. Write a story about the things you would blow on a windy day.

FS-32502 Big Book of Basic Skills

Joy Everywhere

Name _____

Spring Is Coming

Author Unknown

Group 1:   Spring is coming, spring is coming,
Birdies, build your nest;
Weave together straw and feather,
Doing each your best.

Group 2:   Spring is coming, spring is coming,
Flowers are coming too;
Pansies, lilies, daffodillies,
Now are coming through.

All: Spring is coming, spring is coming,
All around is fair;
Shimmer and quiver on the river,
Joy is everywhere.

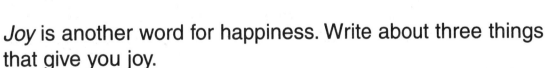

Try This!   *Joy* is another word for happiness. Write about three things that give you joy.

_____

_____

_____

FS-32502 Big Book of Basic Skills

Down the Track

The Railroad Cars Are Coming

Author Unknown

Name _____

Group 1: **The great Pacific railway,**
For California hail!

Group 2: **Bring on the locomotive,**
Lay down the iron rail;

Group 3: **Across the rolling prairies**
By steam we're bound to go,

All: **The railroad cars are coming, humming**
Through New Mexico,
The railroad cars are coming, humming
Through New Mexico.

Group 1: **The little dogs in dog-town**
Will wag each little tail;

Group 2: **They'll think that something's coming**
A-riding on the rail.

Group 3: **The rattlesnake will show its fangs,**
The owl tu-whit, tu-who,

All: **The railroad cars are coming, humming**
Through New Mexico,
The railroad cars are coming, humming
Through New Mexico.

Try This! Imagine that you are taking a trip on a train. Write about what you would see from the train window. Draw a picture of yourself looking out the train window.

The Busy Sun

Name _____

Night

Author Unknown

Speaker 1: The sun that shines all day so bright,
I wonder where he goes at night.

Speaker 2: He sinks behind a distant hill
And all the world grows dark and still,

Speaker 3: And then I go to bed and sleep
Until the day begins to peep.

All: And when my eyes unclose, I see
The sun is shining down on me.

Speaker 4: While we are fast asleep in bed
The sun must go, I've heard it said,

Speaker 5: To other countries far away,
To make them warm and bright and gay.

Speaker 6: I do not know—but hope the sun,
When all his nightly work is done,

All: Will not forget to come again
And wake me through the window-pane.

Try This! List reasons why the sun is important to people everywhere.

_____

_____

_____

_____

Up Tails All!

Name _____

Ducks' Ditty

by Kenneth Grahame

Group 1:   **All along the backwater,**
            Through the rushes tall,
            Ducks are a-dabbling,
            Up tails all!

Group 2:   **Ducks' tails, drakes' tails,**
            Yellow feet a-quiver,
            Yellow bills all out of sight
            Busy in the river!

Group 3:   **Slushy green undergrowth**
            Where the roach swim—
            Here we keep our larder,
            Cool and full and dim!

Group 4:   **Every one for what he likes!**
            ***We* like to be**
            Heads down, tails up,
            Dabbling free!

All: **High in the blue above**
            Swifts whirl and call—
            ***We* are down a-dabbling,**
            Up tails all!

Try This!   Draw a picture that illustrates this poem. Label the things in your picture.

‹240›   FS-32502 Big Book of Basic Skills

Name_____

A Child's Song
adapted

by James Hogg

Speaker 1:   Where the pools are bright and deep,
Where the gray trout lies asleep,
Up the river and o'er the lea

All: That's the way for Billy and me.

Speaker 2:   Where the blackbird sings the latest,
Where the hawthorn blooms the sweetest,
Where the nestlings chirp and flee,

All: That's the way for Billy and me.

Speaker 3:   Where the hazel bank is steepest,
Where the shadow falls the deepest,
Where the clustering nuts fall free,

All: That's the way for Billy and me.

Speaker 4:   So on we go, we love to play
Through the meadow, among the hay;
Up the water and o'er the lea,

All: That's the way for Billy and me.

Try This!   Write about the place in this poem that you would like most to go to. Tell why.

Grasshopper Fun

Name _____

Grasshopper Green

Anonymous

Speaker 1: **Grasshopper Green is a comical chap;**
He lives on the best of fare.

Speaker 2: **Bright little trousers, jacket and cap,**
These are his summer wear.

Speaker 3: **Out In the meadow he loves to go,**
Playing away in the sun;

All: **It's hopperty, skipperty, high and low,**
Summer's the time for fun.

Speaker 4: **Grasshopper Green has a quaint little house;**
It's under the hedge so gay.

Speaker 5: **Grandmother Spider, as still as a mouse,**
Watches him over the way.

Speaker 6: **Gladly he's calling the children, I know,**
Out in the beautiful sun;

All: **It's hopperty, skipperty, high and low,**
Summer's the time for fun.

Try This! Make a list of insects and bugs. Think of as many different kinds as you can.

FS-32502 Big Book of Basic Skills

Name _____

Shell Secrets

Author Unknown

All: **Tell me your secrets, pretty shell,**
I will promise not to tell!

Pair 1:   **Humming, humming, soft and low—**
All about the sea, I know.

Pair 2:   **You are murmuring, I think,**
Of the sea-weeds, green and pink,

Pair 3:   **Of the tiny baby shells**
Where the mother mermaid dwells.

All: **Pretty shell, I'm waiting here,**
Come, and whisper in my ear.

Imagine that you are a shell telling about what you have seen. Finish the sentences.

I have seen _____

I have seen _____

I have seen _____

I have seen _____

I have seen _____

Sailing

Name _____

Boat Song

Anonymous

Group 1: **Lightly row, lightly row!**
O'er the glassy waves we go;

Group 2: **Smoothly glide, smoothly glide**
On the silent tide.

Group 3: **Let the wind and waters be**
Mingled with our melody;

All: **Sing and float, sing and float,**
In our little boat.

Group 1: **Happy we, full of glee,**
Sailing on the waxy sea,

Group 2: **Happy we, full of glee,**
Sailing on the sea.

Group 3: **Luna sheds her softest light**
Stars are sparkling, twinkling bright;

All: **Happy we, full of glee,**
Sailing on the sea.

Try This! Think of three things that can glide. Draw pictures of them.

Name _____

Hiawatha's Brothers

Henry Wadsworth Longfellow

Speaker 1:	**Then the little Hiawatha**
Speaker 2:	**Learned of every bird its language,**
Speaker 3:	**Learned their names and all their secrets;**
Speaker 4:	**How they built their nests in Summer,**
Speaker 5:	**Where they hid themselves in Winter,**
Speaker 6:	**Talked with them whene'er he met them,**
All:	**Called them "Hiawatha's Chickens."**
All:	**Of all beasts he learned the language,**
Speaker 1:	**Learned their names and all their secrets,**
Speaker 2:	**How the beavers built their lodges,**
Speaker 3:	**Where the squirrels hid their acorns,**
Speaker 4:	**How the reindeer ran so swiftly,**
Speaker 5:	**Why the rabbit was so timid,**
Speaker 6:	**Talked with them whene'er he met them**
All:	**Called them "Hiawatha's Brothers."**

Try This! Draw a picture of Hiawatha and his animal "brothers."

Counting Rhyme

Over in the Meadow

Name _____

Traditional

All: **Over in the meadow in the sand in the sun**
Lived an old mother turtle and her little turtle one.
Speaker 1:   **"Dig!" said the mother. "I dig!" said the one.**
All: **So they dug all day in the sand in the sun.**

All: **Over in the meadow where the stream runs blue,**
Lived an old mother fish and her little fishes two.
Speaker 2:   **"Swim!" said the mother. "We swim!" said the two.**
All: **So they swam all day where the stream runs blue.**

All: **Over in the meadow in a hole in a tree,**
Lived an old mother owl and her little owls three.
Speaker 3:   **"Tu-whoo!" said the mother. "Tu-whoo!" said the three.**
All: **So they tu-whooed all day in a hole in a tree.**

All: **Over in the meadow by an old barn door,**
Lived an old mother rat and her little ratties four.
Speaker 4:   **"Gnaw!" said the mother. "We gnaw!" said the four.**
All: **So they gnawed all day by the old barn door.**

All: **Over in the meadow in a snug beehive,**
Lived an old mother bee and her little bees five.
Speaker 5:   **"Buzz!" said the mother. "We buzz!" said the five.**
All: **So they buzzed all day in a snug beehive.**

(continued on page 247

FS-32502 Big Book of Basic Skil

Name _____

All:	Over in the meadow in a nest built of sticks Lived an old mother crow and her little crows six.
Speaker 6:	"Caw!" said the mother. "We caw!" said the six.
All:	So they cawed all day in a nest built of sticks.
All:	Over in the meadow where the grass grows so even Lived an old mother frog and her little froggies seven.
Speaker 7:	"Jump!" said the mother. "We jump!" said the seven.
All:	So they jumped all day where the grass grows so even.
All:	Over in the meadow by the old mossy gate Lived an old mother lizard and her little lizards eight.
Speaker 8:	"Bask!" said the mother. "We bask!" said the eight.
All:	So they basked all day by the old mossy gate.
All:	Over in the meadow by the old scotch pine Lived an old mother duck and her little ducks nine.
Speaker 9:	"Quack!" said the mother. "We quack!" said the nine.
All:	So they quacked all day by the old scotch pine.
All:	Over in the meadow in a cozy wee den Lived an old mother beaver and her little beavers ten.
Speaker 10:	"Beave!" said the mother. "We beave!" said the ten.
All:	So they beaved all day in a cozy wee den.

Try This! Draw a picture that illustrates one of the stanzas in this poem.

Happy Hills

The Hayloft

Robert Louis Stevenson

Group 1:   **Through all the pleasant meadow-side**
The grass grew shoulder-high,
Till the shining scythes went far and wide
And cut it down to dry.

Group 2:   **These green and sweetly smelling crops**
They led in wagons home;
And they piled them here in mountain tops
For mountaineers to roam.

Group 1:   **Here is Mount Clear, Mount Rusty-Nail,**
Mount Eagle and Mount High;
The mice that in these mountains dwell,
No happier are than I!

Group 2:   **O what a joy to clamber there,**
O what a place for play,
With the sweet, the dim, the dusty air,
The happy hills of hay.

Try This!   Paint a picture of a haystack.

〈248〉 FS-32502 Big Book of Basic Skil

Introduction

CHAPTER 9

Math

This chapter has been designed to help all students succeed in math and in working with the concepts of time and money. It provides students with opportunities to practice basic math skills that will help them begin to understand many of the mathematical properties (including time and money) that they will use over and over throughout their lives.

The activities in this chapter have been created to help students feel confident in math computation and in their abilities to understand time and money concepts. In order to ensure success, students must be guided through the activities presented. Each activity features an amusing illustration which will motivate students and help maintain a high level of interest as students complete them. The activities can be used as supplemental material to reinforce any existing math program. Allow students to use models at any time while working on the activities in this chapter.

A variety of fun and simple formats are included throughout the chapter. Students will enjoy completing magic squares, going through paths, coloring shapes and numbers, using rulers, and much more.

The skills covered in this chapter can be taught in the classroom or at home. They include addition and subtraction of two-digit and three-digit numbers (with and without regrouping); estimating sums and differences; shapes; measurement; ordinals through 20th; fractions; graphing; word problems; time to the hour, half-hour, quarter-hour, and five-minute intervals; elapsed time; counting collections of coins including pennies, nickels, dimes, quarters, and half-dollars; problem solving; and critical thinking.

Make Another Ten

Name _____

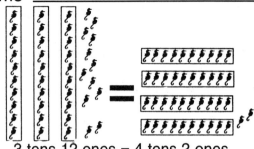

3 tens 12 ones = 4 tens 2 ones

Use 10 of the ones to make another ten.
Write the new numbers.

A.   5 tens 14 ones =

___ tens ___ ones

B.   7 tens 16 ones =

___ tens ___ ones

C.   2 tens 12 ones =

___ tens ___ ones

D.   6 tens 18 ones =

___ tens ___ ones

E.   1 ten   15 ones =

___ tens ___ ones

F.   8 tens 10 ones =

___ tens ___ ones

G.   3 tens 11 ones =

___ tens ___ ones

H.   5 tens 13 ones =

___ tens ___ ones

I.   4 tens 14 ones =

___ tens ___ ones

J.   1 ten   12 ones =

___ tens ___ ones

K.   2 tens 10 ones =

___ tens ___ ones

L.   6 tens 12 ones =

___ tens ___ ones

M.   8 tens 16 ones =

___ tens ___ ones

N.   7 tens 18 ones =

___ tens ___ ones

Jellybean Sums

Adding numbers with
grouping ones

Name _____

Add. Color all the answers that are odd.

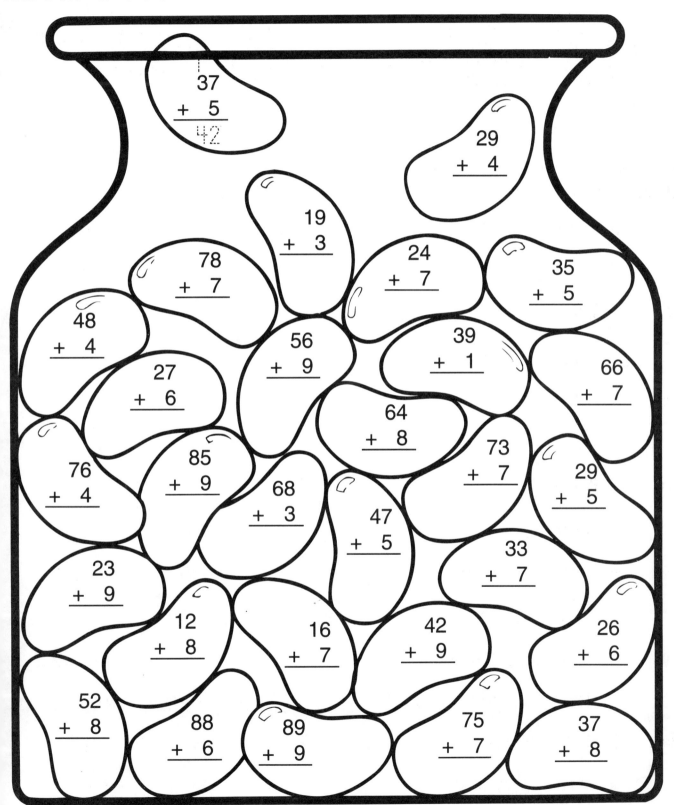

Going on a Trip

Name _____

John is going on a trip. He
needs to take the correct
suitcase. Add the problems.
Color the suitcase that has
answers that are
greater than 152.

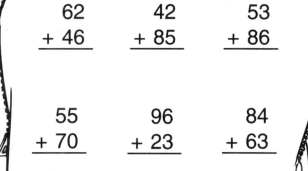

A.
42
+ 95

32
+ 86

65
+ 53

B.

62	42	53
+ 46	+ 85	+ 86

55	96	84
+ 70	+ 23	+ 63

C.

63   75
+ 94   + 80

93   92   61
+ 84   + 97   + 92

D.

73   86
+ 85   + 53

52
88   + 96   78
+ 80   + 31

85   92
+ 43   68   + 47
        + 90

E.

92   35   96
+ 96   + 84   + 62

46   58   79
+ 62   + 81   + 70

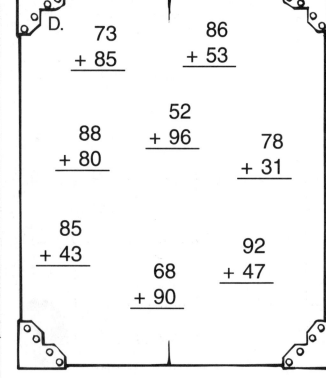

FS-32502 Big Book of Basic Ski

Shapely Squares

Adding 2-digit numbers with regrouping tens and ones

Name _____

Add across and down.

A.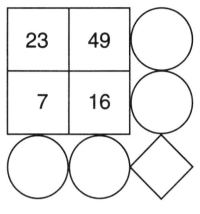

B.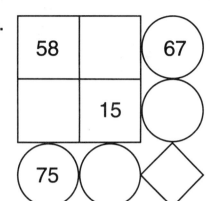

C.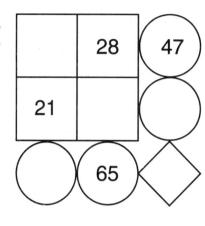

D.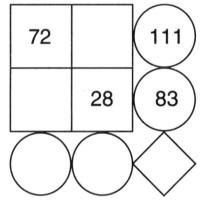

E.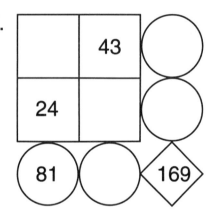

F.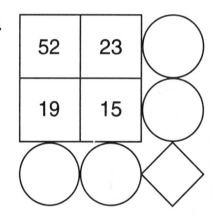

G.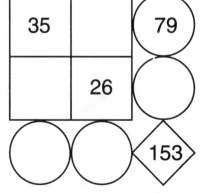

H.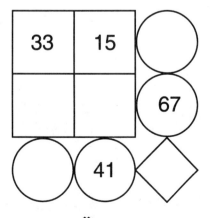

I.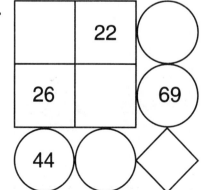

Fishbowl Sums

Name _____

Round each number to the nearest ten. Then add.

48 $\longrightarrow$ ___
+ 23 $\longrightarrow$ +___

19 $\longrightarrow$ ___
+ 61 $\longrightarrow$ +___

33 $\longrightarrow$ ___
+ 18 $\longrightarrow$ +___

42 $\longrightarrow$ ___
+ 48 $\longrightarrow$ +___

29 $\longrightarrow$ ___
+ 53 $\longrightarrow$ +___

12 $\longrightarrow$ ___
+ 21 $\longrightarrow$ +___

34 $\longrightarrow$ ___
+ 56 $\longrightarrow$ +___

73 $\longrightarrow$ ___
+ 18 $\longrightarrow$ +___

41 $\longrightarrow$ ___
+ 29 $\longrightarrow$ +___

39 $\longrightarrow$ ___
+ 43 $\longrightarrow$ +___

81 $\longrightarrow$ ___
+ 13 $\longrightarrow$ +___

22 $\longrightarrow$ ___
+ 67 $\longrightarrow$ +___

62 $\longrightarrow$ ___
+ 17 $\longrightarrow$ +___

44 $\longrightarrow$ ___
+ 37 $\longrightarrow$ +___

63 $\longrightarrow$ ___
+ 28 $\longrightarrow$ +___

11 $\longrightarrow$ ___
+ 83 $\longrightarrow$ +___

Greater Than, Less Than

MATH

Name _____

Subtract. Write < or > in each O to compare the answers.

78 − 16 ○	56 − 38	31 − 15 ○	43 − 26

| 22
− 13
○ | 72
− 27 | 59
− 32
○ | 67
− 19 | 44
− 14
○ | 75
− 37 |

| 95
− 26
○ | 84
− 38 | 70
− 41
○ | 68
− 37 | 79
− 26
○ | 45
− 19 |

| 66
− 34
○ | 30
− 15 | 98
− 5
○ | 83
− 15 | 77
− 23
○ | 92
− 13 |

| 80
− 24
○ | 67
− 48 | 42
− 7
○ | 63
− 29 |

FS-32502 Big Book of Basic Skills

Delightful Differences

Subtracting 2-digit
numbers with regrouping

Name _____

Tom is lost. Help him find the way home.
Subtract. Then shade in all the boxes with odd
numbers to find out which house is his.

83 − 25	75 − 19	42 − 25	54 − 39	63 − 7
31 − 19	60 − 45	22 − 9	43 − 16	55 − 37
53 − 49	64 − 56	71 − 12	85 − 68	92 − 25
73 − 58	86 − 68	28 − 19	32 − 25	62 − 36
80 − 27	91 − 88	78 − 59	93 − 37	51 − 42

FS-32502 Big Book of Basic Skills

Check It Out!

sing addition to check
ubtraction

Name _____

Subtract. Then add to check.

$$\begin{array}{r} \overset{3}{\cancel{4}}\overset{11}{\cancel{1}} \\ -\ 29 \\ \hline 12 \end{array}$$
$$\begin{array}{r} \overset{1}{} \\ 12 \\ +\ 29 \\ \hline 41 \end{array}$$

$$\begin{array}{r} 35 \\ -\ 18 \\ \hline \end{array}$$
$$\begin{array}{r} \underline{} \\ +\ \underline{} \end{array}$$

$$\begin{array}{r} 82 \\ -\ 37 \\ \hline \end{array}$$
$$\begin{array}{r} \underline{} \\ +\ \underline{} \end{array}$$

$$\begin{array}{r} 59 \\ -\ 38 \\ \hline \end{array}$$
$$\begin{array}{r} \underline{} \\ +\ \underline{} \end{array}$$

$$\begin{array}{r} 47 \\ -\ 29 \\ \hline \end{array}$$
$$\begin{array}{r} \underline{} \\ +\ \underline{} \end{array}$$

$$\begin{array}{r} 45 \\ -\ 18 \\ \hline \end{array}$$
$$\begin{array}{r} \underline{} \\ +\ \underline{} \end{array}$$

$$\begin{array}{r} 78 \\ -\ 21 \\ \hline \end{array}$$
$$\begin{array}{r} \underline{} \\ +\ \underline{} \end{array}$$

$$\begin{array}{r} 68 \\ -\ 45 \\ \hline \end{array}$$
$$\begin{array}{r} \underline{} \\ +\ \underline{} \end{array}$$

$$\begin{array}{r} 30 \\ -\ 22 \\ \hline \end{array}$$
$$\begin{array}{r} \underline{} \\ +\ \underline{} \end{array}$$

$$\begin{array}{r} 75 \\ -\ 23 \\ \hline \end{array}$$
$$\begin{array}{r} \underline{} \\ +\ \underline{} \end{array}$$

$$\begin{array}{r} 81 \\ -\ 25 \\ \hline \end{array}$$
$$\begin{array}{r} \underline{} \\ +\ \underline{} \end{array}$$

$$\begin{array}{r} 92 \\ -\ 81 \\ \hline \end{array}$$
$$\begin{array}{r} \underline{} \\ +\ \underline{} \end{array}$$

$$\begin{array}{r} 57 \\ -\ 36 \\ \hline \end{array}$$
$$\begin{array}{r} \underline{} \\ +\ \underline{} \end{array}$$

$$\begin{array}{r} 92 \\ -\ 43 \\ \hline \end{array}$$
$$\begin{array}{r} \underline{} \\ +\ \underline{} \end{array}$$

$$\begin{array}{r} 86 \\ -\ 79 \\ \hline \end{array}$$
$$\begin{array}{r} \underline{} \\ +\ \underline{} \end{array}$$

FS-32502 Big Book of Basic Skills

Rounded Differences

Name _____

Round each number to the nearest ten and subtract.
Circle the answers greater than 45.

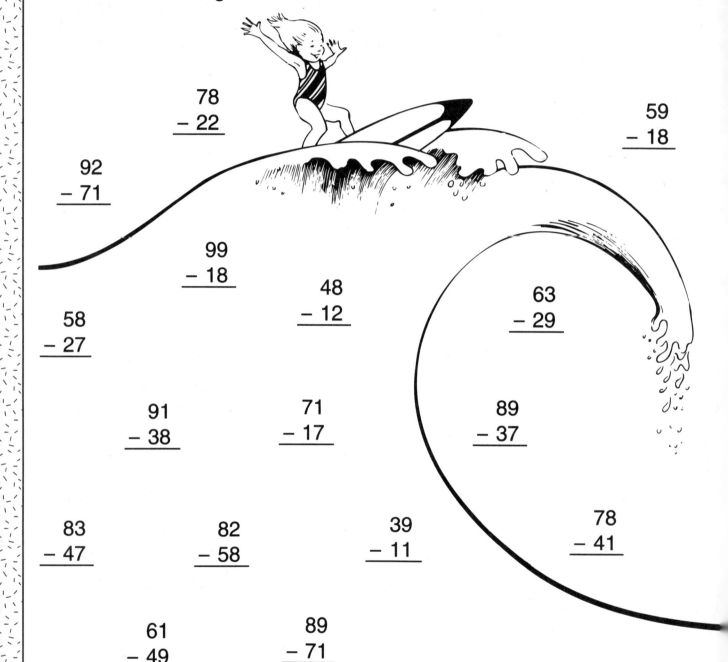

$$78 - 22$$

$$59 - 18$$

$$92 - 71$$

$$99 - 18$$

$$48 - 12$$

$$63 - 29$$

$$58 - 27$$

$$91 - 38$$

$$71 - 17$$

$$89 - 37$$

$$83 - 47$$

$$82 - 58$$

$$39 - 11$$

$$78 - 41$$

$$61 - 49$$

$$89 - 71$$

$$76 - 67 =$$

$$82 - 75 =$$

$$52 - 37 =$$

$$88 - 53 =$$

FS-32502 Big Book of Basic Skills

Family Members

act families, sums to 18

Name _____

Write the sum or difference. Then write the fact family members.

A. $5 + 7 = $ __12__

   $7 + 5 = $ __12__

   $12 - 5 = $ __7__

   $12 - 7 = $ __5__

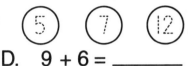

B. $4 + 9 = $ _____

   $9 + 4 = $ _____

   $13 - 4 = $ _____

   $13 - 9 = $ _____

○ ○ ○

C. $8 + 3 = $ _____

   $3 + 8 = $ _____

   $11 - 8 = $ _____

   $11 - 3 = $ _____

○ ○ ○

D. $9 + 6 = $ _____

   $6 + 9 = $ _____

   $15 - 9 = $ _____

   $15 - 6 = $ _____

○ ○ ○

E. $7 + 8 = $ _____

   $8 + 7 = $ _____

   $15 - 7 = $ _____

   $15 - 8 = $ _____

○ ○ ○

F. $5 + 8 = $ _____

   $8 + 5 = $ _____

   $13 - 5 = $ _____

   $13 - 8 = $ _____

○ ○ ○

G. $8 + 9 = $ _____

   $9 + 8 = $ _____

   $17 - 8 = $ _____

   $17 - 9 = $ _____

○ ○ ○

H. $6 + 8 = $ _____

   $8 + 6 = $ _____

   $14 - 6 = $ _____

   $14 - 8 = $ _____

○ ○ ○

I. $7 + 6 = $ _____

   $6 + 7 = $ _____

   $13 - 7 = $ _____

   $13 - 6 = $ _____

○ ○ ○

Write the fact families for the numbers.

J. 5, 6, 11   K. 7, 9, 16

___ + ___ = ___   ___ + ___ = ___   ___ + ___ = ___   ___ + ___ = ___

___ − ___ = ___   ___ − ___ = ___   ___ − ___ = ___   ___ − ___ = ___

FS-32502 Big Book of Basic Skills

What's Missing?

Name _____

Find the missing numbers.

□(1) 5	4 □	□ 7	4 5
+ 3 □(8)	+ 3 6	− 1 □	+ 2 □
————	————	————	————
5 3	8 3	1 9	□ 2

□ 4	1 □	7 2	3 □
− 2 □	+ 5 6	− 1 □	+ □ 9
————	————	————	————
3 6	□ 5	□ 3	6 7

4 □	□ 6	1 □	3 □
+ 1 6	− 3 □	+ 5 4	− □ 7
————	————	————	————
□ 4	2 8	□ 0	1 5

8 □	□ □	□ 7	1 □
− □ 8	− 1 5	+ 3 7	+ 7 8
————	————	————	————
4 0	5 8	6 □	□ 0

□ 9	6 □	9	□ 3
+ 5 □	− □ 3	+ □ □	− 4 9
————	————	————	————
8 9	3 8	4 6	3 □

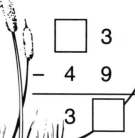

FS-32502 Big Book of Basic Skills

Bull's Eye

Name _____

Write the scores. Write < or > to compare.

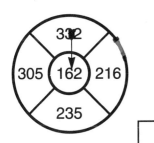 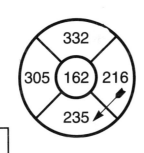

_____ [ ] _____

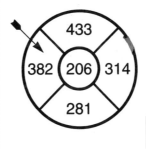 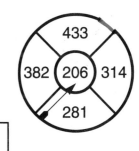

_____ [ ] _____

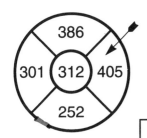 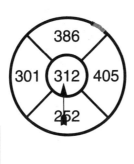

_____ [ ] _____

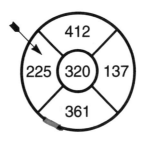 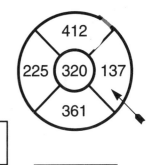

_____ [ ] _____

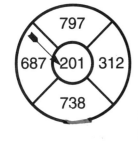 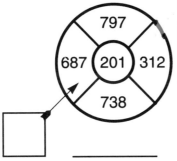

_____ [ ] _____

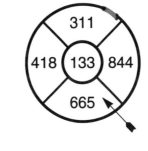 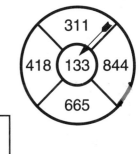

_____ [ ] _____

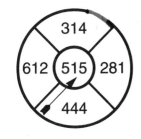 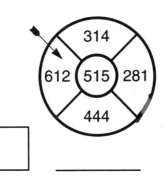

_____ [ ] _____

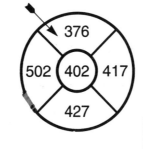 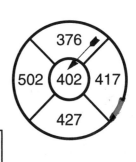

_____ [ ] _____

FS-32502 Big Book of Basic Skills

Ready, Set, Go!

Name _____

Add. Color the animal that wins the race.

$$338 + 171$$

$$247 + 135$$

$$309 + 188$$

$$371 + 291$$

$$528 + 62$$

$$330 + 295$$

$$467 + 125$$

$$232 + 159$$

$$163 + 19$$

$$316 + 339$$

$$463 + 475$$

$$253 + 37$$

$$256 + 183$$

$$526 + 85$$

$$572 + 394$$

$$282 + 438$$

$$281 + 109$$

$$383 + 253$$

$$699 + 8$$

START

264

Color Me Wise

Subtracting 3-digit numbers
without regrouping

Name _____

Subtract.
Use the chart to color the squares.

0 – 199 blue	200 – 399 yellow	400 – 599 green	600 – 799 orange	800 – 999 red

927 – 102 825 r	823 – 102	798 – 503	998 – 456	547 – 425
765 – 612	819 – 9	956 – 325	842 – 512	616 – 100
825 – 315	382 – 270	996 – 92	697 – 25	486 – 286
483 – 171	986 – 581	453 – 441	959 – 129	812 – 112
686 – 86	662 – 352	729 – 321	689 – 578	919 – 106
897 – 81	787 – 116	375 – 14	902 – 401	389 – 380

265

Who Won?

Name _____

Find the differences. Shade in the answers on the trees to see which squirrel makes it to the top.

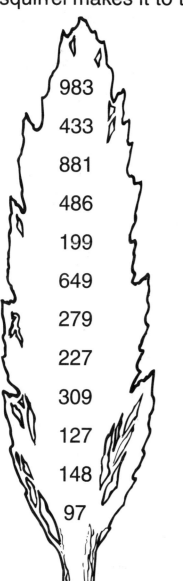

983
433
881
486
199
649
279
227
309
127
148
97

$$\begin{array}{r} 391 \\ -\ 264 \\ \hline \end{array} \qquad \begin{array}{r} 715 \\ -\ 356 \\ \hline \end{array} \qquad \begin{array}{r} 412 \\ -\ 103 \\ \hline \end{array}$$

$$\begin{array}{r} 475 \\ -\ 219 \\ \hline \end{array} \qquad \begin{array}{r} 659 \\ -\ 173 \\ \hline \end{array} \qquad \begin{array}{r} 942 \\ -\ 845 \\ \hline \end{array}$$

$$\begin{array}{r} 632 \\ -\ 391 \\ \hline \end{array} \qquad \begin{array}{r} 378 \\ -\ 99 \\ \hline \end{array} \qquad \begin{array}{r} 964 \\ -\ 745 \\ \hline \end{array}$$

$$\begin{array}{r} 443 \\ -\ 244 \\ \hline \end{array} \qquad \begin{array}{r} 463 \\ -\ 236 \\ \hline \end{array} \qquad \begin{array}{r} 542 \\ -\ 319 \\ \hline \end{array}$$

$$\begin{array}{r} 496 \\ -\ 348 \\ \hline \end{array} \qquad \begin{array}{r} 888 \\ -\ 239 \\ \hline \end{array} \qquad \begin{array}{r} 337 \\ -\ 164 \\ \hline \end{array}$$

135
359
173
356
241
452
365
219
223
225
256
572

$$\begin{array}{r} 538 \\ -\ 182 \\ \hline \end{array} \qquad \begin{array}{r} 462 \\ -\ 237 \\ \hline \end{array} \qquad \begin{array}{r} 605 \\ -\ 172 \\ \hline \end{array} \qquad \begin{array}{r} 733 \\ -\ 281 \\ \hline \end{array}$$

$$\begin{array}{r} 509 \\ -\ 144 \\ \hline \end{array} \qquad \begin{array}{r} 452 \\ -\ 317 \\ \hline \end{array} \qquad \begin{array}{r} 863 \\ -\ 291 \\ \hline \end{array} \qquad \begin{array}{r} 963 \\ -\ 82 \\ \hline \end{array}$$

FS-32502 Big Book of Basic Skills

Follow the Path

Adding and subtracting
2- and 3-digit numbers

Name _____

Add or subtract.

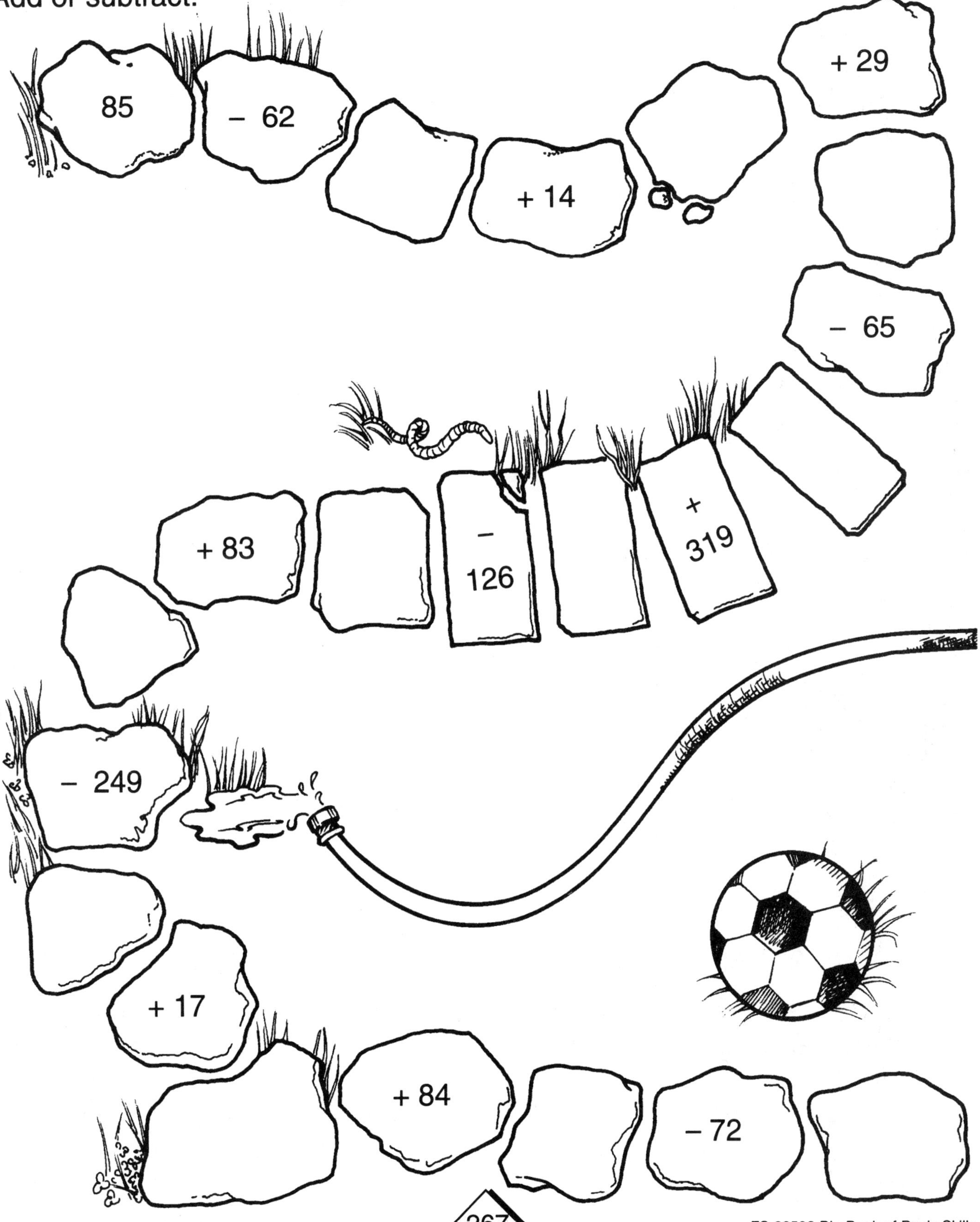

85   − 62   + 14   + 29

− 65

+ 83   − 126   + 319

− 249

+ 17   + 84   − 72

   FS-32502 Big Book of Basic Skills

Patterns

Find the patterns.
Write the missing numbers.

A. 83, 84, 85, _____, 87, _____, _____, _____, 91, _____, _____, 94

B. 346, 345, 344, _____, 342, _____, 340, _____, 338, _____

C. 20, 30, 40, _____, 60, _____, _____, 90, _____, 110, 120, _____

D. 100, 95, 90, _____, 80, 75, _____, _____, 60, _____, _____, _____

E. 100, 200, 300, _____, 500, _____, _____, 800, _____, 1,000

F. 58, 56, 54, _____, 50, _____, 46, _____, _____, _____, 38, _____, 3₄

G. 300, 305, 310, _____, 320, 325, _____, _____, 340, _____

H. 740, 730, 720, _____, 700, _____, 680, 670, _____, 650, 640

I. 1, 3, 5, _____, 9, _____, _____, 15, _____, 19, _____, 23, 25, _____

J. 100, 102, 104, 106, _____, 110, _____, 114, _____, _____

K. 999, 899, 799, _____, 599, _____, _____, 299, _____, 99

L. 4, 8, 12, 16, _____, 24, 28, _____, 36, _____, 44, 48, 52, _____, 60

FS-32502 Big Book of Basic Skills

More, Less, and Equal

Comparing numbers

Name _____

49 > 36	54 < 88	48 = 48
49 is greater than 36.	54 is less than 88.	48 is equal to 48.

Rearrange each set of numbers to solve the math sentences.

A.
3 1 2 4 

3 1 > 2 4
2 3 < 4 1

B.
4 6 7 9

__ __ > __ __
__ __ < __ __

C.
2 3 5 8

__ __ > __ __
__ __ < __ __

D.
6 6 7 7

__ __ > __ __
__ __ < __ __
__ __ = __ __

E.
1 1 8 8

__ __ > __ __
__ __ < __ __

F.
5 5 9 9

__ __ > __ __
__ __ < __ __

G.
1 2 3
6 7 8

__ __ __ > __ __ __
__ __ __ < __ __ __

H.
0 1 4
5 8 9

__ __ __ > __ __ __
__ __ __ < __ __ __

I.
2 3 4
5 6 9

__ __ __ > __ __ __
__ __ __ < __ __ __

To the Top!

Name _____

Color the ants:

    red—thirteenth and second

    blue—seventh and nineteenth

    green—sixth and tenth

    yellow—seventeenth and first

    black—eleventh and fourth

    purple—twentieth and third

    orange—eighth and eighteenth

    pink—fifteenth and fifth

    tan—sixteenth and twelfth

    gray—fourteenth and ninth

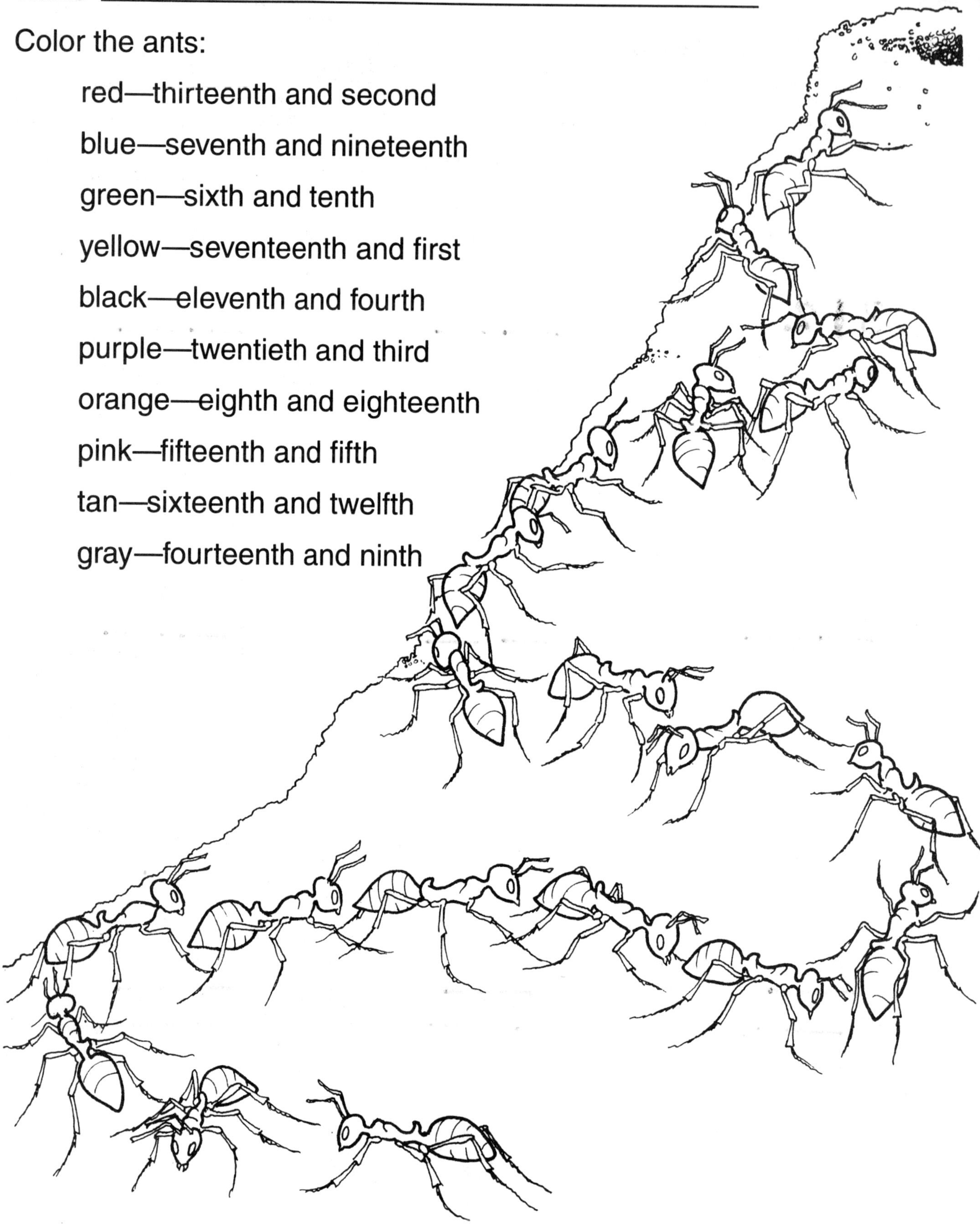

270

Fraction Fun

Name _____

Color using the code below.

1/2 = yellow	2/3 = blue
1/3 = red	2/4 = orange
1/4 = purple	3/4 = tan

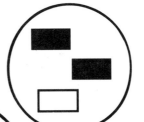

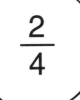

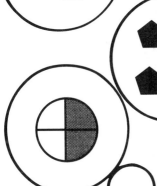
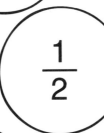

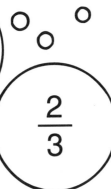

FS-32502 Big Book of Basic Skills

Flowerbed Fractions

Fraction

Name _____

There are 4 presents.
1 of them has a bow.
The matching fraction is ¼.

Follow the directions below.

☐ Color ⅚ of the tulips red. Color ⅙ of them yellow.

☐ Color ⅔ of the daffodils yellow. Leave ⅓ of them white.

☐ Color ¼ of the daisies purple. Color ¾ of them orange.

☐ Leave ⅘ of the worms white. Color ⅕ of them yellow.

☐ Color ½ of the butterflies orange. Color ½ of them blue.

☐ Color the soil brown and the stems and leaves green.

272

Tiptop Shape

Name _____

Count how many of each shape. Then color.

Name	Shape	Number	Color
Circle	◯		yellow
Square	▢		red
Triangle	△		blue
Rectangle	▭		green

Do You Measure Up?

Name _____

Guess the length of each object. Then use a centimeter ruler to measure the objects. Were you close?

A.

Guess: _____ cm

Actual: _____ cm

B.

Guess: _____ cm

Actual: _____ cm

C.

Guess: _____ cm

Actual: _____ cm

D.

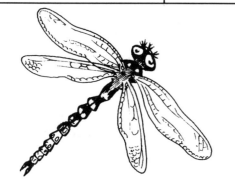

Guess: _____ cm   Actual: _____ cm

E.

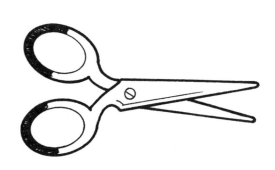

Guess: _____ cm   Actual: _____ cm

F.

Guess: _____ cm

Actual: _____ cm

G.

Guess: _____ cm

Actual: _____ cm

H.

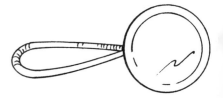

Guess: _____ cm

Actual: _____ cm

FS-32502 Big Book of Basic Skills

All the Way Around

Name _____

Use a centimeter ruler. Measure each side. Add.

A.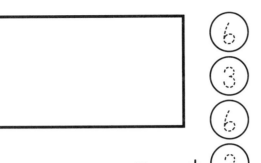

$\begin{array}{r} 6 \\ 3 \\ 6 \\ + \ 3 \\ \hline 18 \end{array}$ cm

B.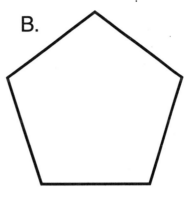

+ _____

_____ cm

C.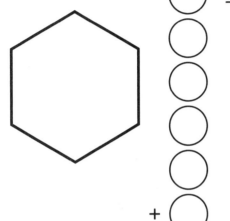

+ _____

_____ cm

D.

+ _____

_____ cm

E.

$\bigcirc + \bigcirc + \bigcirc + \bigcirc =$ _____ cm

F.

$\bigcirc + \bigcirc + \bigcirc + \bigcirc =$ _____ cm

G.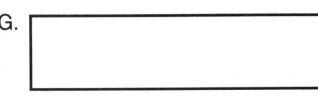

$\bigcirc + \bigcirc + \bigcirc + \bigcirc =$ _____ cm

H.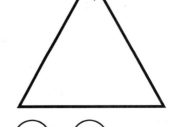

$\bigcirc + \bigcirc + \bigcirc =$ _____ cm

FS-32502 Big Book of Basic Skills

Balls of Fun

Name _____

Shade in a square for each ball.

8					
7					
6					
5					
4					
3					
2					
1					
	A	B	C	D	E

Use the graph to answer the questions.

1. What ball has the greatest number? _____

2. How many A's and D's are there altogether? _____

3. Which two balls have the same number? _____

4. How many more C's are there than D's? _____

5. What ball has the least number? _____

6. How many E's and B's are there altogether? _____

7. How many A's, B's, and D's are there altogether? _____

8. How many more B's than E's are there? _____

Line Up

gic

Name _____

Four children are in a line. Read each set of clues.
Write each child's name on the matching line.

A.

1. _____ 2. _____ 3. _____ 4. _____

Clues

- Ali is between Amy and Andy.
- April is last.
- Amy is only next to Ali.

B.

1. _____ 2. _____ 3. _____ 4. _____

Clues

- Maria and Mimi are in the middle.
- Mike is next to Mimi.
- Matt is not first.

Token Arcade

Name _____

 25 tokens
 48 tokens
 37 tokens
 53 tokens

 19 tokens
 16 tokens
 9 tokens
 62 tokens

Write addition or subtraction number sentences. Then solve.

A. How much will a ball and a comic cost? _73 tokens_	25 +48 ―― 73	B. How much will a bear and a pencil cost? _____	
C. How much will a jump rope and a whistle cost? _____		D. How much will a ring and a set of jacks cost? _____	
E. How much more does a bear cost than a comic? _____		F. How much more does a ring cost than a bear? _____	
G. How much less does a jump rope cost than a ball? _____		H. How much will a jump rope and a set of jacks cost? _____	

I. Make up your own problem. Solve it. Then ask a friend to solve it, too.

_____

_____

_____

FS-32502 Big Book of Basic Skil

School Play

Name _____

Make up number sentences and solve.

1. Rosemont School is putting on a play. There are 75 first-grade students and 108 second-grade students in the play. How many students are in the play?

$$\begin{array}{r} 75 \\ +108 \\ \hline 183 \end{array}$$ students

2. The art teacher made 975 programs to hand out at the play. At the end of the play, there were 486 programs left. How many programs were given out that night?

3. The All-Purpose Room seats 850 people. There were 535 people at the play. How many seats were empty?

4. Snacks and sodas were sold after the play. There were 288 candy bars, and all but 65 were sold. How many candy bars were sold?

5. Max filled 324 bags with popcorn. By the end of the evening, 189 were sold. How many bags of popcorn were left?

6. There were 358 adults and 94 children at the play. How many people were at the play in all?

7. The students raised $745 selling tickets and snacks. They spent $68 for a cast party. How much do they have left to give to the school?

Two-Way Times

Name _____

Write each time using numbers and words.

A.

_____

_____

B.

_____

_____

C.

_____

_____

D.

_____

_____

E.

_____

_____

F.

_____

_____

G.

_____

_____

H.

_____

_____

FS-32502 Big Book of Basic Skil

Lasso the Time

me to the hour and half-hour

Name _____

Circle the correct times.

A.    4:30 5:30 6:30

B. 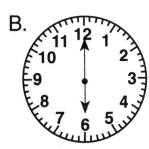 12:00 12:30 6:00

C. 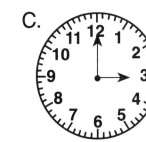   12:00 3:00 4:00

D.    10:30 11:30 12:30

E. 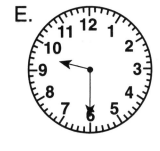 9:30 10:30 8:30

F. 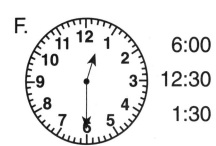 6:00 12:30 1:30

G.    10:00 11:00 12:00

H.   8:00 9:00 12:00

I. 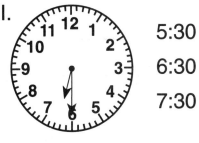 5:30 6:30 7:30

J. 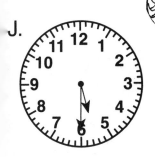   5:30 6:30 7:50

Frank Schaffer Publications, Inc.

FS-32502 Big Book of Basic Skills

Make a Match

Name _____

Draw lines to match the times.

A.

10:45   6:15   12:45

B.

7:15   7:45   8:15

C.

1:45   2:15   2:45

FS-32502 Big Book of Basic Ski

Quarter-Hour Times

Name _____

Write each time using numbers and words.

A.

_____

_____

B.

_____

_____

C.

_____

_____

D.

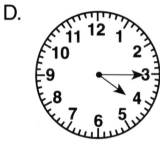

_____

_____

E.

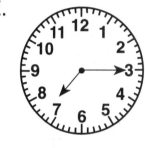

_____

_____

F.

_____

_____

G.

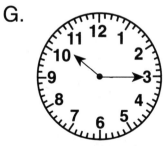

_____

_____

H.

_____

_____

Secret Message

Name _____

Match each clock to the word telling its time. Cut out the times at the bottom of the page. Paste the times in the boxes.

TOP SECRET

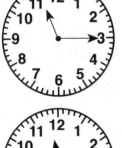

quarter to 8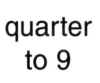

quarter to 9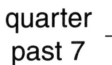

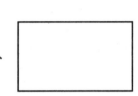

quarter past 7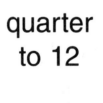

quarter to 12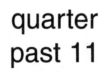

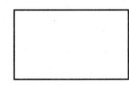

quarter past 11

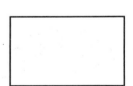

| 8:45 | 7:45 | 7:15 | 11:15 | 11:45 |

284

The Hands of Time

Name _____

Draw hands to show the times.

A.

8:15

B.

9:45

C.

quarter past 5

D.

quarter to 11

E.

11:45

F.

quarter past 9

G.

quarter to 3

H.

6:15

I.

3:15

J.

quarter to 1

285

After Hours

Name _____

Count the minutes by fives. Complete the times.

A.

_____ minutes
past _____

_____

B.

_____ minutes
past _____

_____

C.

_____ minutes
past _____

_____

D.

_____ minutes
past _____

_____

E.

_____ minutes
past _____

F.

_____ minutes
past _____

_____

G.

_____ minutes
past _____

_____

H.

_____ minutes
past _____

_____

FS-32502 Big Book of Basic Sk

Just Before

Time to five-minute intervals, :30–:00

Name _____

Count the minutes by fives. Complete the times.

A.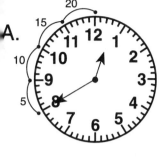

_____ minutes
to _____

_____

B.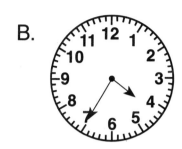

_____ minutes
to _____

_____

C.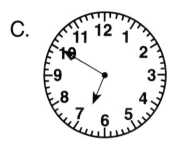

_____ minutes
to _____

_____

D.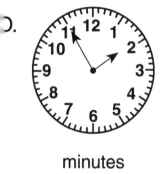

_____ minutes
to _____

_____

E.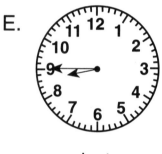

_____ minutes
to _____

_____

F.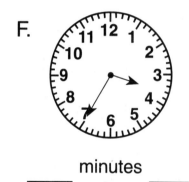

_____ minutes
to _____

_____

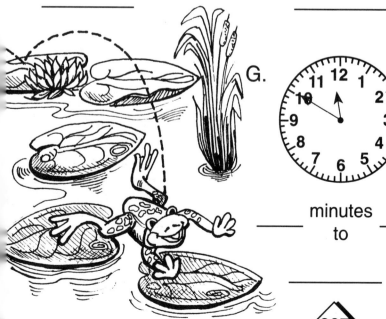

G.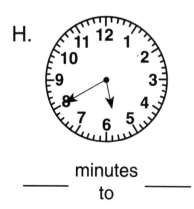

_____ minutes
to _____

_____

H.

_____ minutes
to _____

_____

Frank Schaffer Publications, Inc.

FS-32502 Big Book of Basic Skills

Bloomin' Times

Name _____

Match the clocks to the correct times.

A. 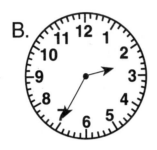   B.   C.   D.

E. 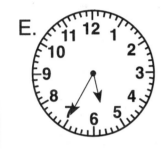   F.

2:35	5:35
11:25	10:40
3:30	10:10
7:50	9:20
8:00	4:35
12:55	12:45
6:15	5:05

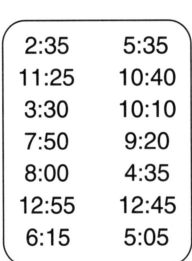

G.   H.

I.   J.

K. 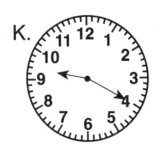   L.    M.    N.

FS-32502 Big Book of Basic Sk

The Right Time

Name _____

Circle the correct times.

A.

7:10

8:10

2:07

B.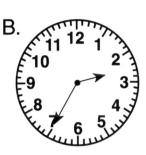

7:12

2:35

2:40

C.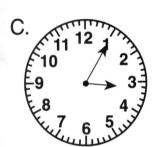

1:15

2:05

3:05

D.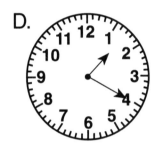

1:20

2:20

4:05

E.

8:50

9:50

10:45

F.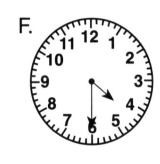

4:35

4:30

6:20

G.

11:25

12:25

5:00

H.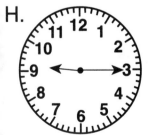

8:15

9:15

10:15

I.

10:40

11:40

7:50

J.

11:05

12:55

1:55

FS-32502 Big Book of Basic Skills

Words Can Tell

Name _____

Match the clocks with the times.

A.

| 20 minutes past 7 | 20 minutes past 8 | 20 minutes to 8 |

B.

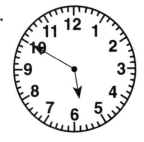

| 10 minutes past 5 | 10 minutes to 6 | 10 minutes to 5 |

C.

| 25 minutes to 2 | 25 minutes past 1 | 25 minutes to 1 |

FS-32502 Big Book of Basic Skills

A Timely Riddle

Name _____

Write the times. Then solve the puzzle.

M.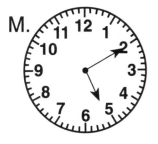

O.

T.

N.

_____ _____ _____ _____

A.

I.

R.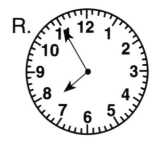

E.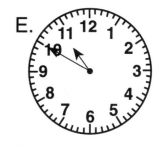

_____ _____ _____ _____

U.

K.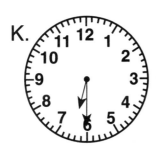

F.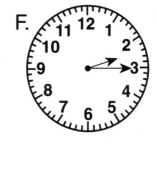

_____ _____ _____ _____

_____ _____ _____ _____   _____ _____ _____ _____
5:10   9:40   6:30   10:50   4:25   12:25   5:10   10:50

                                                                    !
_____ _____ _____   _____ _____ _____
2:15   11:35   7:55   2:15   8:30   1:05

© Frank Schaffer Publications, Inc.   FS-32502 Big Book of Basic Skills

Time Marches On

Name _____

Write the times. Tell how many hours have elapsed.

A.

from _____ to _____

_____ hour(s)

B.

from _____ to _____

_____ hour(s)

C.

from _____ to _____

_____ hour(s)

D.

from _____ to _____

_____ hour(s)

E.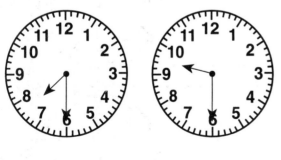

from _____ to _____

_____ hour(s)

FS-32502 Big Book of Basic Skill

One Hour Later

Elapsed time, critical thinking

Name _____

Write the times. Write the times one hour later.
Draw hands on the clocks to match.

A.

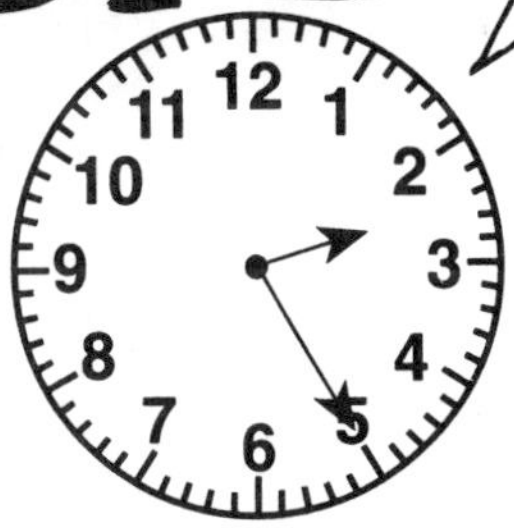

_____ ➔ _____

B.

_____ ➔ _____

C.

_____ ➔ _____

D.

_____ ➔ _____

E.

_____ ➔ _____

FS-32502 Big Book of Basic Skills

Toy Time

Name _____

Count. Write the cost of each toy in the price tag.

A.

B.

C.

D.

E.

F.

294

Pay the Clerk

Name _____

Color the coins you need to buy each hat.

A.

B.

C.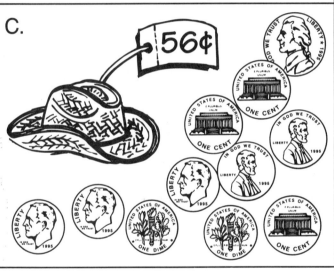

D.

E.

F.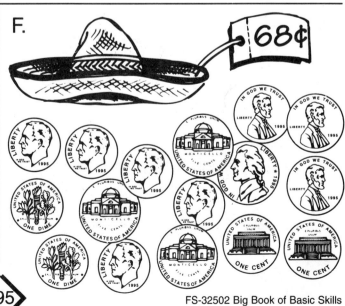

FS-32502 Big Book of Basic Skills

What's Left?

Problem solving with mone

Name _____

You have	You buy	What's left?
A.	 17¢	
B.	 22¢	
C.	 41¢	
D.	 57¢	
E.	 36¢	

296

Boxed Collections

Value of a quarter

Name _____

Make each box worth a quarter.
Cross out coins you don't need.
Remember:

25¢

A.

B.

C.

D.

E.

F.

G.

FS-32502 Big Book of Basic Skills

School Store

Name _____

Cut out the prices tags. Count the money. Paste the price tags beside the items to show what they cost.

A.

B.

C.

D.

E.

F.

 40¢   75¢   50¢   65¢ 35¢ 55¢

298

FS-32502 Big Book of Basic Skills

Is There Enough Money?

Counting on from quarters, critical thinking

Name _____

Is there enough money to go on the ride?
Write the amounts. Then circle **yes** or **no**.

A.

_____ yes no

B.

_____ yes no

C.

_____ yes no

D.

_____ yes no

E.

_____ yes no

F.

_____ yes no

G.

_____ yes no

© Frank Schaffer Publications, Inc.

299

FS-32502 Big Book of Basic Skills

Furry Friends for Sale

Name _____

Circle the coins you need to buy each stuffed animal.

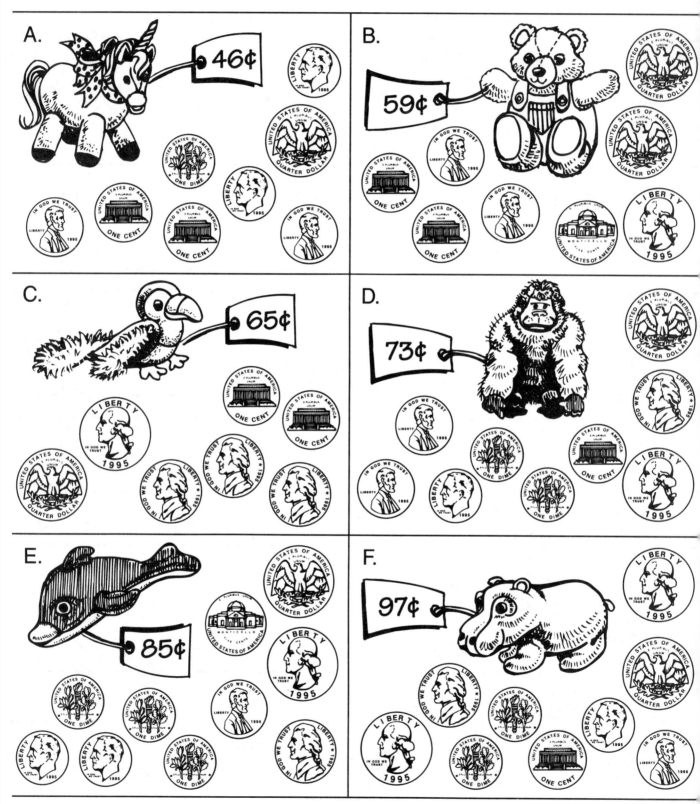

A. 46¢

B. 59¢

C. 65¢

D. 73¢

E. 85¢

F. 97¢

FS-32502 Big Book of Basic Skills

Star-Studded Collections

Name _____

Write the amounts. Color the stars.

50¢ – 74¢ = yellow   75¢ – 99¢ = red

A.

_____

B.

_____

C.

_____

D.

_____

E.

_____

F.

_____

FS-32502 Big Book of Basic Skills

Solve and Draw

Name _____

Solve the riddles.
Draw the coins.

A. There are 4 coins. They are worth 16¢. What are the coins?

B. There are 3 coins. They are worth 21¢. What are the coins?

C. There are 5 coins. They are worth 47¢. What are the coins?

D. There are 7 coins. They are worth 79¢. There are no dimes. What are the coins?

E. There are 6 coins. They are worth 40¢. What are the coins?

F. There are 5 coins. They are worth 95¢. What are the coins?

Have a Half

Value of a half-dollar

Name _____

Add one coin to make each
collection worth a half-dollar.

Remember:

50¢

A.

B.

C.

D.

E.

F.

G.

FS-32502 Big Book of Basic Skills

Money Match

Name _____

Match each set of coins to the correct amount.

A.    85¢

B.    61¢

C.    63¢

D.    77¢

E.    81¢

F.    53¢

G.    95¢

FS-32502 Big Book of Basic Skills

Sunny Money

Name _____

Circle the correct amounts.

A.

77¢ 86¢ 95¢

B.

70¢ 80¢ 90¢

C.

63¢ 73¢ 83¢

D.

77¢ 88¢ 99¢

E.

56¢ 68¢ 77¢

F.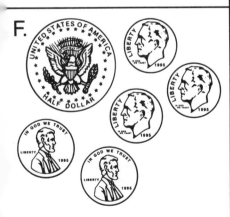

82¢ 87¢ 92¢

G.

78¢ 88¢ 98¢

H.

85¢ 90¢ 95¢

FS-32502 Big Book of Basic Skills

Is There Anything Left?

Name _____

Complete the coins and amounts to make change. Write the amount of change you will get.

You Have	You Buy	You Get			Change Amount
A.	2¢	3¢	4¢	5¢	3¢
B.	3¢				
C.	7¢				
D.	5¢				
E.	3¢				
F.	4¢				

FS-32502 Big Book of Basic Skill

Funny Money

ounting coin collections

Name _____

Write the amount of money in each set.

A.   $_____

B.  $_____

C.      $_____

D.     $_____

E. $_____

F.  $_____

G. $_____

H.     $_____

Name _____

Draw the bills and coins you need to buy each item.

A.

$1.32

B.

$.91

C.

$1.75

D.

$.77

E.

$.96

F.

$1.26

G.

$.85

H.

$1.23

FS-32502 Big Book of Basic Ski

Make a Decision

Name _____

Circle the coins you need to buy the items. If you do not have enough money, circle NOT ENOUGH.

A.

NOT ENOUGH

B.

NOT ENOUGH

C.

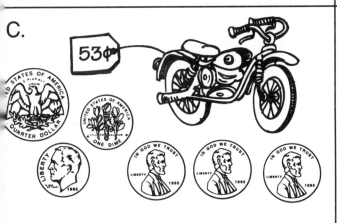

NOT ENOUGH

D.

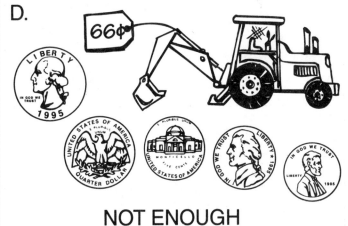

NOT ENOUGH

E.

NOT ENOUGH

F.

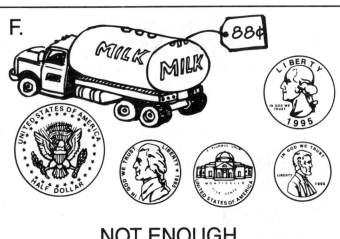

NOT ENOUGH

Answers

PHONICS

Page 36
1. camp　　2. tent　　3. map
4. catch　　5. best　　6. west
7. ten

Page 37
1. Mom (box)　　2. mix (circle)
3. box (box)
4. milk (circle)
5. mix (circle); thick (circle)
6. hot (box)
7. sizzle (circle)
8. flip (circle)
9. big (circle)
10. It (circle)

Page 38
1. up　　2. sun　　3. Ben
4. wet　　5. fun　　6. truck
7. shells

Page 39
bat, sock, cup, cat, duck, fish, nest, pin, desk, lock

Page 40
1. white, ice, polar bear
2. cave, mane, lion
3. stripe, home, skunk
4. ride, vine, monkey
5. huge, nose, elephant

Page 41
mule, fire, lake;
rose, tube, mice;
whale, stove, cube;
bike, cane, bone

Page 42
cake, tube, bike;
fire, bone, wheel;
cube, game, bee;
nose, tree, plate

Page 43
1. gray　　2. Ray　　3. tail
4. hay　　5. pail　　6. grain
7. rain　　8. train

Page 44
1. read　　2. feather　　3. head
4. bread　　5. thread　　6. instead

Page 45
1. peach　　2. leaf　　3. wheels
4. heel　　5. beach　　6. sweet
7. bee　　8. feet

Page 46
1. boat　　2. load　　3. coat
4. float　　5. soaked　　6. coast

Page 47
4, 7, 6, 3
1, 8, 2, 5
y as in *funny*: bunny, baby, penny, sunny
y as in *my*: cry, fry, sky, fly

Page 48
blue: table, gate, rope, tube, bee, cube
brown: desk, hat, pig, fish, stick, doll

Page 49
long—cake, feet, pipe, mule, soap, sale, cube, be, hope, dime
short—step, hat, pig, up, mop, job, hill, nut, tap, flag

Page 50
Circle the following: cent, corn, face, cook, mice, cube.
soft c: cent, face, mice
hard c: corn, cook, cube

Page 51
green: go, good, grows, garden, gold
blue: gym, giant, stage, giant, vegetables, gems

Page 52
shell, thimble, thumb, shirt, ship, shoe, sheep, think

Page 53
1. fish, shells, beach
2. chickens, sheep, farm
3. shopping, shoes, mall
4. Pitch, Chop, camp
5. Chase, bench, park

Page 54
wh, whale　　　　　ch, chair
ch, chimney　　　　wh, wheel
ch, chick　　　　　ch, chalk
wh, whisper　　　　ch, church

Page 55
score, swim, skate
snake, skunk, swan
snow, ski, sled
stars, story, sleep

Page 56
sk—orange, sl—red, sp—purple, sm—green, sn—brown, st—blue, sn—brown, sk—orange, sn—brown, sk—orange, sl—red, sm—green

Page 57
bread, drum, frog, dress, train, crown, grapes, tree, broom, frame, truck, prize

Page 58
4, 2, 8, 7
1, 5, 6, 3
Sentences will vary.

Page 59
1. school　　2. zoo　　3. broom
4. pool　　5. hoot　　6. moon
7. tooth

Page 60
1. look, book, library
2. hook, brook, brook
3. took, hoof, horseshoe
4. wood, good, logs
5. cook, good, cook

Page 61
book—took, hook, good, foot, hood, cook, wood, stood, shook, look
boot—tool, moon, school, room, tooth, roof, soon, pool, mood, zoo

Page 62
1. art　　2. cart　　3. shark
4. stars　　5. farm　　6. Mark

Page 63
Circle the following: boy, coin, toy, Roy, oil, foil.
oi: coin, oil, foil
oy: boy, toy, Roy

Page 64
1. mouse　　2. crown　　3. cow
4. count　　5. owl　　6. brown
7. snow　　8. house

Page 65
lamb—b, wreath—w, knife—k, write—w comb—b, knob—k, knit—k, limb—b, thumb—b

Page 66
string, hang, ring
sink, sting, skunk
wing, swing, strong
junk, sing, trunk

Page 67
run, running　　　　clap, clapping
bat, batting　　　　win, winning
1. bat　　2. batting　　3. run
4. clapping　　5. winning

Answers

GRAMMAR

Page 69
These underlined sections of sentences should be rewritten as complete sentences:

<u>Thick fur.</u>
<u>Bears also.</u>
<u>Usually have twins.</u>
<u>Brown bears largest.</u>

Page 70
1. My best friend is Denise.
2. She is a very good ice skater.
3. Denise can do fancy turns.
4. She is teaching me how to skate.
5. Sometimes I fall on the hard ice. or Sometimes I fall hard on the ice.
6. I like to skate backwards.
7. We have fun skating together.

Page 71
Answers will vary but all should be subjects so that the sentences are complete.

Page 72
Answers will vary but all should be predicates so that the sentences are complete.

Page 73
Answers will vary but all should be silly sentences made by matching up the subjects and predicates.

Page 74
Answers will vary but all should be declarative sentences about the flower.

Page 75
Answers will vary but all five should be a question relating to a tiger.

Page 76
1. A ? 2. T . 3. T . 4. A ?
5. T . 6. T . 7. T . 8. A ?
9. A ? 10. T . 11. T . 12. A ?
13. T . 14. T .

Page 77
Answers will vary but all should be written exclamations.

Page 78
Wow, look how big it is!
How do they know dinosaurs didn't drag their tails?
Machines make these dinosaur models move.
Which was the biggest dinosaur?
Watch out!

Paleontologists are scientists who study dinosaurs.
Could we go on a dinosaur dig?
This is a claw of a tyrannosaurus.
What did stegosaurus use its plates for?
Thank you!

Page 79
1. Go to our office.
2. Open the red door.
3. Find the shortest robot.
4. Look for its blue knob.
5. Turn the knob three times.
6. Tell the robot to come to us.

Page 80
The birds, sailboats, clouds, umbrellas, Snack Bar, and girls should be colored. Written nouns will vary.

Page 81
1. Teresa 2. Brian 3. Fluffy
4. *Crow Boy* 5. Friday 6. May
7. Texas 8. New York City
9. Saturn 10. Mrs. Stone

Page 82
A. 5 chairs   F. 3 crayons
B. 3 desks   G. 2 pencils
C. 9 rabbits   H. 2 computers
D. 2 books   I. 2 clocks
E. 2 globes   J. 3 plants

Page 83

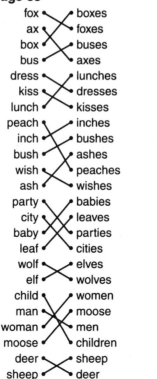

Page 84
1. friends 2. heat 3. spoon
4. bowls 5. cubes 6. spoons
7. seconds 8. minute

Page 85
The scenes in the picture depicting the following verbs should be colored: swings, balance, drinking, step, bow, follows. Written verbs will vary.

Page 86
1. am 2. is 3. am 4. is
5. are 6. are 7. Are 8. are
9. is 10. am

Page 87
1. is 2. live 3. make 4. hunt
5. eat 6. uses 7. sleep 8. have

Page 88

Page 89

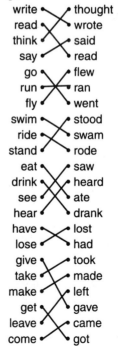

Answers

Page 90

1. left   2. rode   3. got
4. ran   5. sang   6. made
7. drew   8. wrote   9. gave
10. put   11. told   12. sat

Page 91

The scenes in the picture depicting the following adjectives (Wibbles) should be colored to match these adjectives: tall, round, bumpy, happy, sad, and young. Written adjectives will vary.

Page 93

short — slowest
tall — shortest
slow — fastest
fast — tallest
nice — nicest
late — biggest
hot — latest
big — saddest
sad — hottest
happy — messiest
funny — happiest
messy — funniest

(taller, slower, shorter, later, faster, hotter, sadder, nicer, bigger, funnier, messier, happier)

Page 94

1. an   2. a   3. a   4. a
5. a   6. a   7. a   8. an
9. a   10. an   11. a   12. an
13. a   14. an   15. an   16. a
17. a   18. a   19. a   20. a

Page 95

1. it   2. he   3. she   4. it
5. they   6. she   7. he   8. they
9. I   10. we

Page 96

1. us   2. it   3. them
4. me   5. him   6. her

Page 97

Answers will vary. Possible answers include:

1. quickly   2. loudly   3. neatly
4. carefully   5. badly   6. slowly
7. proudly   8. quietly   9. happily

MECHANICS

Page 99

1. Lucy—Lovey
2. Susie—Sassie
3. Henry—Hairy
4. Felicia—Fluffy
5. Merrill—Marty
6. Angela—Angel
7. Peter—Pumpkin

8. Gordon—Goldie
9. Lucy's pet is Lovey.
10. Susie's pet is Sassie.
11. Henry's pet is Hairy.
12. Felicia's pet is Fluffy.
13. Merrill's pet is Marty.
14. Angela's pet is Angel.
15. Peter's pet is Pumpkin.
16. Gordon's pet is Goldie.

Page 100

1. David likes to go to Disneyland.
2. Ollie likes to go to Oceans of Fun.
3. Bob likes to go to Barnett Baseball Park.
4. Adam likes to go to Adventure Landing.
5. Halie likes to go to Harrisonville History Museum.
6. Sue likes to go to Super City Science Museum.

7.–12. These answers can be in any order: Columbia Zoo, Jerry's Ice Cream Parlor, Waterworld, Mount Rushmore, Pete's Petting Park, David's Department Store.

Page 101

1. Sharks   2. There   3. They
4. Some   5. They   6. Other
7. The   8. Sharks   9. They
10. Some   11. Be   12. Sharks
13. They   14. If

Page 102

1. I went to the dentist.
2. Jan and I ride our bikes to school.
3. I like to read funny books.
4. My mom said I can go swimming.
5. I love pizza.
6. Can I come too?
7. Will I get a treat today?
8.–10. Answers will vary.

Page 103

1. Sunday
2. Monday
3. Saturday
4. Friday
5. Saturday and Sunday
6. Wednesday
7. Tuesday and Thursday
8. Saturday and Sunday
9. Answers will vary.
10. Monday, Tuesday, Wednesday, Thursday, Friday

Page 104

1. January   2. February
3. March   4. April
5. May   6. June
7. July   8. August
9. September   10. October
11. November   12. December

30 days: April, June, September, November

31 days: January, March, May, July, August, October, December

28 days: February

Page 105

Answers may vary but below are the most probable answers students will write.

1. Labor Day is in September.
2. Mother's Day is in May.
3. Father's Day is in June.
4. St. Patrick's Day is March 17.
5. Thanksgiving Day is in November.
6. Martin Luther King, Jr.'s birthday is in January.
7. Independence Day is July 4.
8. New Year's Day is January 1.

Page 106

1. L.R.T.   2. S.R.F.   3. M.K.K.
4. T.M.R.   5. C.W.S.   6. T.L.J.
7. M.J.B.   8. T.J.M.
9.–14. Answers will vary.

Page 107

1.–6. Any of the following are appropriate: Dear, To, Dearest.

7.–12. Any of the following are appropriate: Your friend, Love, As always, Yours truly.

Page 108

1. June   2. Dear   3. Thank
4. We   5. I   6. The
7. I   8. Chuck   9. He
10. There   11. Love   12. Jessica

Page 109

California, Oregon, Oregon, Washington, Montana, Missouri

1.–10. Answers will vary.

Page 110

Students can use any combination of names, streets, cities, states, and ZIP codes they like as long as each is used only once.

Page 111

Answers will vary.

Answers

Page 112
1. Cinderella
2. Little Red Riding Hood
3. Sleeping Beauty
4. Goldilocks and the Three Bears
5. The Wizard of Oz
6. The Gingerbread Boy
7.–10. Answers will vary.

Page 113

It's Raining

It's raining,
It's pouring,
The old man is snoring.
He went to bed.
He bumped his head,
And he couldn't get up
In the morning.

Page 114

Have you ever heard of John F. Kennedy? He was the youngest man ever elected president of the United States. He was also the youngest man ever to die in office.

Did you know that John F. Kennedy was only 43 when he was elected president? How much older than you was he when he was elected?

Kennedy had three brothers and five sisters. How would you like to have eight brothers and sisters in your family? Kennedy was born in Massachusetts, but his family moved often. Have you ever moved?

Many people loved President Kennedy. It was a very sad day when he was killed. This man will never be forgotten.

Page 115

Answers will vary.

Page 116
1. Whee!
2. I'm so proud!
3. Way to hit that ball, Annie!
4. Catch it, Joe!
5. Hurry! We're late!
6. Ouch!
7. Be careful, Kayla!
8. Oh, you poor thing!

Page 117
1. Tuesday—Tues.
2. March—Mar.
3. October—Oct.
4. Wednesday—Wed.
5. January—Jan.
6. Sunday—Sun.
7. February—Feb.
8. September—Sept.
9. November—Nov.
10. Monday—Mon.
11. August—Aug.
12. Saturday—Sat.
13. Friday—Fri.
14. December—Dec.
15. April—Apr.
16. Thursday—Thurs.

Page 118
1. wouldn't
2. aren't
3. doesn't
4. isn't
5. couldn't
6. shouldn't
7. he'll
8. they'll
9. it'll
10. she'll
11. we'll
12. you'll
13. she'll, doesn't
14. We'll
15. It'll
16. isn't
17. don't
18. I'll, you'll
19. Won't

Page 119
1. g   2. d   3. h   4. j
5. b   6. c   7. a   8. f
9. e   10. i

Page 120
1. Katy's lunchbox
2. Kevin's bat
3. Paul's book
4. Robin's sweater
5. Kara's soccer ball
6. Peter's backpack
7. Chandler's shoes
8. Troy's mitt
9. Beth's umbrella

Page 121
1. "Do you like riddles?" asked Andrew.
2. "Yes, I like riddles," said Tommy.
3. "What is black and white and read all over?" asked Andrew.
4. "A newspaper," said Tommy.
5. "You're right," said Andrew.
1.–7. Answers will vary.

Page 122

Emily: Birthday—May 4, 1982
Stephanie: Birthday—July 14, 1986
Uncle Joe: Birthday—October 28, 1963
Michael: Birthday—April 17, 1994
Brittney: Birthday—March 10, 1993
Grandpa: Birthday—June 6, 1935;
Anniversary—March 2, 1958
Grandma: Birthday—May 30, 1938;
Anniversary—March 2, 1958

Mom: Birthday—January 21, 1959;
Anniversary—June 4, 1979
Dad: Birthday—August 9, 1957;
Anniversary—June 4, 1979
Fluffy: Day we brought her home—
December 26, 1990

Page 123
1. Westmoreland County, Virginia
2. Hardin, Kentucky
3. Atlanta, Georgia
4. Hope, Arkansas
5. East St. Louis, Illinois
6. Allegheny, Pennsylvania
7. Newburgh, New York
8. Los Angeles, California
9. Cambridge, Ohio

Page 124
1. Kari is going to bring spoons, forks, and knives.
2. Alan is going to bring soda pop, juice, and lemonade.
3. Larry is going to bring apples, grapes, and cherries.
4. Sandie is going to bring chips, peanuts, and pretzels.
5. Jeff is going to bring a bat, a ball, and a mitt.
6. Susie is going to bring a tablecloth, plates, and napkins.
7. Sandie's mom is bringing Alan, Kari, and Sandie to the picnic.
8. Jeff's mom is bringing Jeff, Susie, and Larry to the picnic.

Page 125
1. June 21, 1997; Dear Mom,; Lots of love,
2. June 22, 1997; Dear Joey,; Lots of love,
3. June 23, 1997; Dearest Mother,; Your loving son,
4. June 24, 1997; Dear Joey,; Your loving mother,

Page 126

Yesterday, we went to the zoo. We saw elephants, zebras, and giraffes. "I like the monkeys best," I said to my teacher. "What is your favorite animal?" I asked her. She told me she likes giraffes the best. I think I'll go to the zoo again soon. I love it!

Page 127
1. One   2. Saturday   3. May
4. Janie   5. She   6. I
7. That   8. Janie   9. She
10. How   11. Make   12. Spaceship
13. On   14. Pine   15. Street
16. We   17. Then   18. Janie
19. So   20. Boy   21. No

SPELLING

Page 129
1. cat, hat   2. man, van
3. can, bag   4. map
5. sad   6. fast   7. hand

Page 130
1. jet   2. red   3. ten
4. leg   5. hen   6. yes
7. many   8. well   9. went
10. wet

Page 131
pig, him, is, big, sit, it
1. did   2. been
3. win   4. if

Page 132
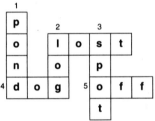
1. frog   2. got   3. want   4. not

Page 133
1. fun   2. but   3. from
bus, stuck, mud;
run, of, rug, must

Page 134
they, say, play,
today, wait, way
1. rain
2. train
3. paint; said

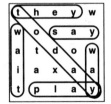

Page 135
1. ate, plate   2. name, same
3. came   4. bake   5. have
6. lake   7. made   8. tape

Page 136
1. be, beach   2. green, piece
3. sleep, week   4. team, three
5. read, me   6. three
7. week   8. me
9. beach   10. green
11. sleep   12. piece
13. be

Page 137
Order of answers may vary.
1. mind   2. find   3. kind
4. nice, time   5. five, nine   6. give
7. I, live   8. live

Page 138
1. by   2. sky   3. fly
4. my   5. b**uy**   6. dr**y**
7. ri**gh**t   8. ni**gh**t   9. li**gh**t
10. hi**gh**

Page 139
1. home   2. rope   3. old
4. note   Solution: hole
5. go   6. no   7. come
8. open   9. rode   10 gone

Page 140
1. snow   2. road   3. know
4. slow   5. low   6. goat
7. coat   8. boat   9. bowl
10. soap

Page 141
1. s**oo**n, sch**oo**l   2. l**oo**se, z**oo**
3. t**u**ne, fl**u**te   4. too
5. cool   6. boot
7. rule   Solution: tool

Page 142
1. **c**orn   2. **c**lock   3. **k**ite
4. bla**ck**   5. **c**ake   6. **k**id
7. cook   8. rock   9. lock
10. pick

Page 143
1. state   2. slide   3. snap
4. speak   5. spoke   6. story
7. slept   8. snake   9. sled
10. stop

Page 144
1. bring   2. plant   3. Friday
4. clean   5. please   6. plane
7. free   8. class   9. friend
10. bread

Page 145
1. start   2. hard   3. large
4. warm   5. dark   6. far
7. farm   8. car   9. part
10. are

Page 146
girl, dirt, hurt, her, shirt;
1. turn   2. worm   3. jerk
4. first   5. work

Page 147
1. best   2. ask   3. behind
4. stand   5. jump   6. sand
7. desk   8. camp   9. mask
10. last

Page 148
1. four, for
2. won, one
3. ate, eight
4. hear, here
5. hour, our

Order of answers may vary: four, hour, hear, eight, won.

Page 149
1. thank   2. with   3. mother
4. tooth   5. than   6. father
7. the   8. this   9. then
10. that

Page 150
1. what   2. when   3. wheel
4. whale   5. white   6. why
7. where   8. whose   9. which
10. who

Page 151
children, lunch, each, cheese, finish, wash;
1. shop   2. wish, she
3. much

Page 152
1. brown, house, town
2. loud, sound, owl
3. round   4. out
5. down   6. now

Page 153
1. look   2. bush   3. book
4. good   5. put   6. pull
7. push   8. foot   9. full
10. took

Page 154
baby, only, very;
1. carry   2. puppy   3. funny
4. penny   5. happy   6. easy
7. pretty

Page 155

1. beets, beans
2. meats
3. cherries
4. dishes
5. pears
6. peaches
7. eggs
8. berries
9. boxes

Page 156

1. hugged 2. stepped 3. ripped
4. tapping 5. hopping 6. tap
7. hop 8. rip 9. hug
10. step

Page 157

1. anyone 2. everyday
3. something 4. without
5. sunlight 6. football
7. homework 8. backpack
9. inside 10. bedroom

Page 158

1. it's 2. we're 3. You'll
4. haven't 5. don't 6. what's
m, can't, they're, isn't

VOCABULARY DEVELOPMENT

Page 160

1. vacation 2. dunes 3. shells
4. tide 5. waves 6. ocean
7. beach

Page 161

Snowflake: December, January, February
Leaf: March, April, May
Sun: June, July, August
Pumpkin: September, October, November

Page 162

1. twenty 2. thirty 3. fifty
4. sixty 5. ten 6. ninety
7. seventy 8. eighty 9. forty

Page 163

1. principal 2. librarian
3. custodian 4. secretary
5. nurse 6. teacher

Page 164

1. refrigerator 2. ingredients
3. boil 4. stove
5. bake, broil 6. oven
7. recipe

Page 165

1. penny 2. half-dollar 3. dime
4. quarter 5. nickel 6. dollar

Page 166

Page 167

1. Sunday 2. Tuesday
3. Friday 4. Saturday
5. Monday 6. Thursday
7. Wednesday

Page 168

1. joey 2. kitten 3. pup
4. duckling 5. foal 6. calf
7. cub 8. chick

Page 169

1. a. skyscrapers b. bustling
   c. illuminated d. atmosphere
2. Sentences will vary.

Page 170

1. polygon with 6 sides
2. polygon with 5 sides
3. polygon with 8 sides
4. polygon with 7 sides
5. polygon with 4 sides
6. polygon with 3 sides

Page 171

Page 172

1. uncle 2. aunt
3. cousins 4. grandmother
5. grandfather 6. daughter
7. son

Page 173

1. fifth 2. eighth 3. second
4. tenth 5. first 6. third
7. sixth 8. fourth 9. seventh
10. ninth

Page 174

1. to, two 2. ate, eight
3. maid, made 4. hear, here
5. see, sea

Page 175

1. Thanksgiving
2. Hanukkah, Kwanzaa, Christmas
3. Cinco de Mayo
4. no
5. yes
6. no
7. Answers will vary.

Page 176

Magnets are objects that can attract other objects. Magnets have two poles, one on each end. One pole is positive and is marked with a (+). The other pole is negative and is marked with a (–). Two positive charges or two negative charges push away from each other, or repel. Positive and negative charges attract, or draw toward, each other; metals

Page 177

1. solar energy 2. protect
3. conserve 4. recycle
5. polluting 6. polluting
7. recycling

Page 178

1. biography 2. science
3. history 4. fiction
5. nonfiction

Page 179

Most people in the United States of America speak English. In Mexico, most people speak Spanish. People in Israel speak Hebrew. In Greece, people speak Greek. The main language spoken in Italy is Italian. People in France speak French.

1. English 2. Spanish
3. French 4. Hebrew
5. Greek 6. Italian

Page 180

1. a dividing line formed in combing hair
2. a role in a play
3. to stop being with another person
4. to break or divide into sections
5. a necessary piece
6. a portion, or share

Page 181
1. tired
2. went down
3. choices
4. hurt
5. switch
6. figure out

Page 182
1. moon   2. Earth   3. planets
4. space   5. solar system
6. universe   7. star
meteors

Page 183

```
e x m r z a m r (c y c l e) d v x
(c o n d e n s a t i o n) n h a m
r c n d (e a r t h) e s s e o p i
t e u (p r e c i p i t a t i o n)
h a t d v r a m e l l o o r r i
t n e (e v a p o r a t i o n) t o
```

Page 184
1. George Washington
2. Susan B. Anthony
3. Thomas Edison
4. Alexander Graham Bell
5. Benjamin Franklin

Page 185
1. delighted
2. easy
3. cover up
4. right
5. evening
6. ask

Page 186
1. keyboard
2. monitor
3. printer
4. modem
5. diskette
6. computer
7. hard copy

Page 187
1. Dunes
2. ingredients
3. Roots
4. cub
5. Wednesday
6. skyscrapers
7. hexagon
8. seventh

Page 188
1. Cinco de Mayo
2. magnet
3. Recycle
4. fiction
5. Options
6. planet
9. disappointed
8. computer

READING COMPREHENSION

Page 190
1. Maria, a school, first
2. It was Maria's first day at her new school.

Page 191
1. the kind of animal Casey loves.
2. all kinds of dogs.
3. False

Page 192
1. Brad wants to go to the swimming pool.
2. Brad wants to go to a cool place.
3. (A) and (B) can be variations on any two of the following: He wants to play on his raft; he wants to swim, dive, and splash; he wants to wear his swimsuit in the cold blue water; he wants to go to a cool place.

Page 193
1. Nat
2. pickles
3. Nat loves pickles!

Page 194
1. Kim wants to go to the zoo.
2. Kim's mom can't go because she is busy.
3. The butterfly is blue.
4. Kim saw the brown cricket on her hand.

Page 195
1. Sandie—go to the pool, eat pizza, stay up late, jump rope;
   Taylor—ride a bike, eat pizza, dig for dinosaur bones, stay up late
2. 4
3. stay up late

Page 196
1. pink
2. bike rack
3. They both have yellow handlebars.
4. Lori
5. False

Page 197
1. Teddy woke up.
2. Teddy got dressed.
3. Teddy brushed his teeth.
4. Mama Bear called Teddy to breakfast.
5. Teddy cleaned his room.

Page 198
1. Paste half of an empty eggshell on a piece of cardboard.
2. 2—Pile…; 3—Put…; 4—Pour…

Page 199
1. Students color Rocky Coyote brown.
2. balloons
3. forks
4. pretty rocks
5. Hilda Hamster
6. pizza
7. camera
8. radio

Page 200
1. large fish
2. killer whales
3. *Killer whale, killer whales*, or *whale* should be circled in the paragraph.
4. Answers will vary.
5. A blue X should be drawn on top of "mean" in the second line of the paragraph.

Page 201
Page should be completed according to the directions.

Page 202
1. she planted it in good soil, watered it, and put it in a sunny spot.
2. did not grow.
3. good soil, water, sunlight

Page 203
1. he stepped in a puddle.
2. washed his shoes.
3. It was raining.
4. his mom got home.

Page 204
1. it will turn into a ball.
2. become different colors.
3. painting it after it dries.

Page 205
1. Jason and Amber
2. cheese
3. hamster, cat
4. Answers will vary.

Page 206
1. fish
2. in the water.
3.–4. Answers will vary.

Page 207
Answers will vary but could include:
1. happy, surprised, glad, pleased
2. sad, unhappy, mad
3. helpful, kind   4. bossy
5. pleased, happy, glad, nice

Page 208
1. kind
2. shy
3. mean
4. bossy

Page 209
Fanny—trusting; Frieda—certain; Farah—helpful; Frankie—mean

Answers

Page 210
1. They will fall off the trees.
2. fall or autumn; winter.
3. Answers will vary but could include coats, hats, mittens, boots, gloves, and jackets.
   Answers will vary but could have something to do with it being cold.

Page 211
1. Mom gave them carrot and bean seeds.
2. Katelyn and Tommy planted the seeds.
3. Later, the plants started to grow.

Page 212
1. It goes to look for food.
2. peep for food.
3. Answers should be some variation on the idea that the baby birds will learn to fly, will fly away from the nest, or will grow.

Page 213
1. school.   2. True   3. False
4. True   5. helpful

Page 214
1. Answers will vary but should have something to do with the ants needing to prepare food and take care of eggs and babies.
2. Answers will vary but should note that the eggs would be in danger and could be hurt or damaged.
3. help grow a fungus.
4. they use it for food.

Page 215
1. Birds should be colored blue.
2. Number two should be circled in red.
3. Worms should be colored brown.
4. Spring should be circled.

Page 216
1. wheels, motors, headlights
2. Answers will vary but could include the following: people can take either one to work; they both are made of the same kinds of materials; both have windows.
3. Answers may vary but could include the following: some buses have more wheels than cars; buses have more windows than cars; buses can carry more people than cars; a bus is much bigger than a car; cars have seat belts, but most buses do not.

Page 217
1. Both   2. Spot   3. Spot
4. Scooter   5. Both

Page 218
1. have fins; swim; have teeth
2. Sharks live alone, are fish, and have gills.
   Dolphins have lungs and are mammals.

Page 219
1. Circle wings, eyes.
2. a, d, f

MATH

Page 250
A. 6 tens 4 ones   B. 8 tens, 6 ones
C. 3 tens, 2 ones   D. 7 tens, 8 ones
E. 2 tens, 5 ones   F. 9 tens, 0 ones
G. 4 tens, 1 one   H. 6 tens, 3 ones
I. 5 tens, 4 ones   J. 2 tens, 2 ones
K. 3 tens, 0 ones   L. 7 tens, 2 ones
M. 9 tens, 6 ones   N. 8 tens, 8 ones

Page 251
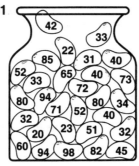

Page 252
A. 137, 118, 118
B. 108, 127, 139, 125, 119, 147
C. 157, 155, 177, 189, 153
D. 158, 139, 168, 148, 109, 128, 158, 139
E. 188, 119, 158, 108, 139, 149
Greater than 152 = suitcase C

Page 253
A. 72; 23; 30, 65, 95
B. 9; 17, 32; 24, 99
C. 19; 37, 58; 40, 105
D. 39; 55; 127, 67, 194
E. 57, 100; 45; 69; 88
F. 75; 34; 71, 38, 109
G. 44; 48; 74; 83, 70
H. 48; 41; 26; 74, 115
I. 18, 40; 43; 65, 109

Page 254
50 + 20 = 70, 20 + 60 = 80,
30 + 20 = 50, 40 + 50 = 90, 30 + 50 = 80,
10 + 20 = 30, 30 + 60 = 90, 70 + 20 = 90,
40 + 30 = 70, 40 + 40 = 80, 80 + 10 = 90,
20 + 70 = 90, 60 + 20 = 80, 40 + 40 = 80,
60 + 30 = 90, 10 + 80 = 90

Page 255

		52	12	22
21	21	15	25	30
31	13	25	7	10
36	24	44	24	22
40	55	51	33	51
14	10	24		

Page 256
A. 4, 13   B. 6, 11   C. 3, 16
D. 2, 12   E. 8, 14   F. 7, 15
G. 5, 16   H. 8, 10   I. 6, 15
J. 3, 11   K. 1, 18   L. 5, 10

Page 257

62 > 18	16 < 17	
9 < 45	27 < 48	30 < 38
69 > 46	29 < 31	53 > 26
32 > 15	93 > 68	54 < 79
	56 > 19	35 > 34

Page 258
58, 56, **17**, **15**, 56
12, **15**, **13**, **27**, 18
4, 8, **59**, **17**, 67
15, 18, **9**, **7**, 26
53, **3**, **19**, 56, **9**

Page 259
12, 17, 45; 21, 18, 27;
57, 23, 8; 52, 56, 11;
21, 49, 7

Page 260
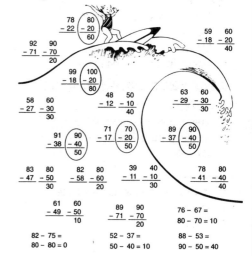

Answers

Page 261

A. 12, 12, 7, 5; 5, 7, 12
B. 13, 13, 9, 4; 4, 9, 13
C. 11, 11, 3, 8; 3, 8, 11
D. 15, 15, 6, 9; 6, 9, 15
E. 15, 15, 8, 7; 7, 8, 15
F. 13, 13, 8, 5; 5, 8, 13
G. 17, 17, 9, 8; 8, 9, 17
H. 14, 14, 8, 6; 6, 8, 14
I. 13, 13, 6, 7; 6, 7, 13
J. 5 + 6 = 11, 6 + 5 = 11,
11 − 5 = 6, 11 − 6 = 5
K. 7 + 9 = 16, 9 + 7 = 16,
16 − 7 = 9, 16 − 9 = 7

Page 262

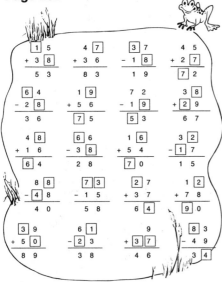

Page 263

378 < 567; 696 > 639
657 < 698; 586 > 549
939 < 999; 976 < 977
829 < 893; 878 > 819

Page 264

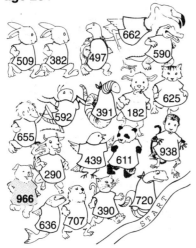

Page 265

825 r	721 r	295 y	542 g	122 b
153 b	810 r	631 o	330 y	516 g
510 g	112 b	904 r	672 o	200 y
312 y	405 g	12 b	830 r	700 o
600 o	310 y	408 g	111 b	813 r
816 r	671 o	361 y	501 g	9 b

Page 266

```
  391      715      412
− 264    − 356    − 103
  127      359      309

  475      659      942
− 219    − 173    − 845
  256      486       97

  632      378      964
− 391    −  99    − 745
  241      279      219

  443      463      542
− 244    − 236    − 319
  199      227      223

  496      888      337
− 348    − 239    − 164
  148      649      173
```

```
  538      462      605      733
− 182    − 237    − 172    − 281
  356      225      433      452

  509      452      863      963
− 144    − 317    − 291    −  82
  365      135      572      881
```

Squirrel on right made it to the top.

Page 267

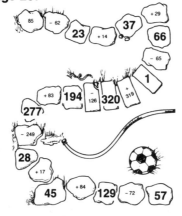

Page 268

A. 86, 88, 89, 90, 92, 93
B. 343, 341, 339, 337
C. 50, 70, 80, 100, 130
D. 85, 70, 65, 55, 50, 45
E. 400, 600, 700, 900
F. 52, 48, 44, 42, 40, 36
G. 315, 330, 335, 345
H. 710, 690, 660
I. 7, 11, 13, 17, 21, 27
J. 108, 112, 116, 118
K. 699, 499, 399, 199
L. 20, 32, 40, 56

Page 269

Answers will vary.

Page 270

Page 271

Page 272

Page 273

Answers may vary. 13 circles,
5 squares, 3 triangles, 29 rectangles

Page 274

A. 5.5 cm B. 5.2 cm C. 3.4 cm
D. 5.5 cm E. 6.5 cm F. 3 cm
G. 2 cm   H. 5.5 cm

FS-32502 Big Book of Basic S

Answers

Page 275
A. $6 + 3 + 6 + 3 = 18$
B. $3 + 3 + 3 + 3 + 3 = 15$
C. $2 + 2 + 2 + 2 + 2 + 2 = 12$
D. $3 + 5 + 3 + 5 = 16$
E. $3 + 3 + 3 + 3 = 12$
F. $2 + 2 + 2 + 2 = 8$
G. $2 + 8 + 2 + 8 = 20$
H. $4 + 4 + 4 = 12$

Page 276
1. C
2. 6
3. A and B
4. 5
5. D
6. 7
7. 10
8. 1

Page 277
A. 1. Amy 2. Ali 3. Andy 4. April
B. 1. Mike 2. Mimi 3. Maria 4. Matt

Page 278
A. $25 + 48 = 73$ tokens
B. $53 + 9 = 62$ tokens
C. $19 + 16 = 35$ tokens
D. $62 + 37 = 99$ tokens
E. $53 - 48 = 5$ tokens
F. $62 - 53 = 9$ tokens
G. $25 - 19 = 6$ tokens
H. $19 + 37 = 56$ tokens
I. Problems and solutions will vary.

Page 279
1. $75 + 108 = 183$ students
2. $975 - 486 = 489$ programs
3. $850 - 535 = 315$ empty seats
4. $288 - 65 = 223$ sold
5. $324 - 189 = 135$ bags left
6. $358 + 94 = 452$ people
7. $\$745 - \$68 = \$677$ left

Page 280
A. 2:30; half past 2
B. 6:00; 6 o'clock
C. 10:00; 10 o'clock
D. 3:00; 3 o'clock
E. 9:30; half past 9
F. 5:30; half past 5
G. 11:00; 11 o'clock
H. 12:30; half past 12

Page 281
A. 4:30   B. 6:00   C. 3:00
D. 11:30   E. 9:30   F. 12:30
G. 10:00   H. 9:00   I. 6:30
J. 5:30

Page 282
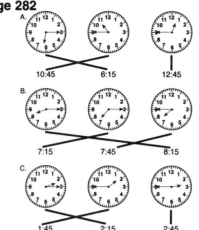

Page 283
A. 2:15; quarter past 2
B. 11:45; quarter to 12
C. 12:15; quarter past 12
D. 4:15; quarter past 4
E. 7:15; quarter past 7
F. 6:45; quarter to 7
G. 10:15; quarter past 10
H. 3:45; quarter to 4

Page 284
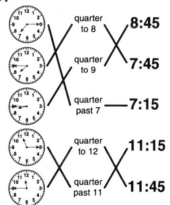

Page 285
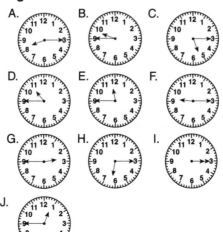

Page 286
A. 5 minutes past 9; 9:05
B. 10 minutes past 7; 7:10
C. 15 minutes past 6; 6:15
D. 20 minutes past 3; 3:20
E. 25 minutes past 1; 1:25
F. 30 minutes past 5; 5:30
G. 10 minutes past 10; 10:10
H. 5 minutes past 12; 12:05

Page 287
A. 20 minutes to 1; 12:40
B. 25 minutes to 5; 4:35
C. 10 minutes to 7; 6:50
D. 5 minutes to 2; 1:55
E. 15 minutes to 9; 8:45
F. 25 minutes to 4; 3:35
G. 10 minutes to 12; 11:50
H. 20 minutes to 6; 5:40

Page 288
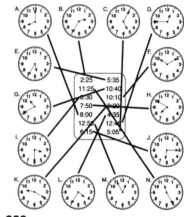

Page 289
A. 7:10   B. 2:35   C. 3:05
D. 1:20   E. 8:50   F. 4:30
G. 11:25   H. 9:15   I. 10:40
J. 12:55

Page 290
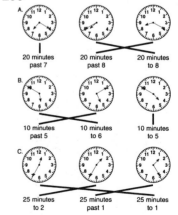

Page 291
MAKE TIME FOR FUN!

Page 292

A. 2:00 to 3:00; 1 hour
B. 5:00 to 7:00; 2 hours
C. 3:30 to 4:30; 1 hour
D. 10:00 to 1:00; 3 hours
E. 7:30 to 9:30; 2 hours

Page 293

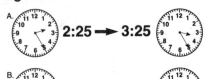
A. 2:25 → 3:25

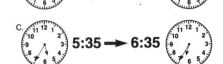
B. 8:50 → 9:50

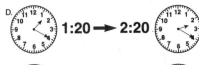
C. 5:35 → 6:35

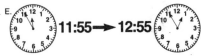
D. 1:20 → 2:20

E. 11:55 → 12:55

Page 294

A. 33¢   B. 55¢   C. 45¢
D. 72¢   E. 84¢   F. 93¢

Page 295

A. Students should color 3 dimes, 1 nickel, and 2 pennies.
B. Students should color 7 dimes and one penny.
C. Students should color 5 dimes, 1 nickel, and 1 penny.
D. Students should color 3 dimes, 1 nickel, and 4 pennies.
E. Students should color 3 dimes, 2 nickels, and 3 pennies, or 2 dimes, 4 nickels, and 3 pennies.
F. Students should color 6 dimes, 1 nickel, and 3 pennies, or 5 dimes, 3 nickels, and 3 pennies.

Page 296

A. 37¢; 20¢   B. 52¢; 30¢   C. 43¢; 2¢
D. 58¢; 1¢   E. 47¢; 11¢

Page 297

A. Students should cross out 1 nickel and 4 pennies.
B. Students should cross out 1 dime.
C. Students should cross out 2 nickels.
D. Students should cross out 1 penny.
E. Students should cross out 1 nickel and 3 pennies.
F. Students should cross out 3 dimes and 4 pennies.
G. Students should cross out 2 dimes, 1 nickel, and 4 pennies.

Page 298

A. 40¢   B. 35¢   C. 50¢
D. 55¢   E. 65¢   F. 75¢

Page 299

A. 75¢; yes   B. 65¢; no
C. 75¢; yes   D. 70¢; no
E. 85¢; yes   F. 75¢; yes
G. 55¢; no

Page 300

A. Students should circle 1 quarter, 2 dimes, and 1 penny.
B. Students should circle 2 quarters, 1 nickel, and 4 pennies.
C. Students should circle 2 quarters and 3 nickels.
D. Students should circle 2 quarters, 2 dimes, and 3 pennies.
E. Students should circle 2 quarters, 3 dimes, and 1 nickel.
F. Students should circle 3 quarters, 2 dimes, and 2 pennies.

Page 301

A. 52¢; yellow   B. 62¢; yellow
C. 77¢; red   D. 72¢; yellow
E. 75¢; red   F. 98¢; red

Page 302

A. 3 nickels and 1 penny
B. 2 dimes and 1 penny
C. 1 quarter, 2 dimes, 2 pennies
D. 3 quarters, 4 pennies
E. 2 dimes, 4 nickels
F. 3 quarters, 2 dimes

Page 303

A. Add a nickel.
B. Add a dime.
C. Add a penny.
D. Add a dime.
E. Add a penny.
F. Add a dime.
G. Add a penny.

Page 304

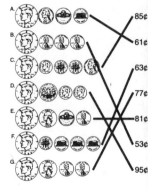

Page 305

A. 86¢   B. 80¢   C. 63¢   D. 88¢
E. 68¢   F. 82¢   G. 78¢   H. 90¢

Page 306

	You Have	You Buy	You Get	Change Amount
A.		● 2¢	3¢ 4¢ 5¢	3¢
B.		● 3¢	4¢ 5¢	2¢
C.		7¢	8¢ 9¢ 10¢	3¢
D.		● 5¢	5¢	5¢
E.		● 3¢	4¢ 5¢ 10¢	7¢
F.		4¢	5¢ 10¢	6¢

Page 307

A. $1.23   B. $.86   C. $1.70
D. $1.35   E. $.92   F. $1.63
G. $.85   H. $1.42

Page 308

Answers will vary.

A. one $1 bill, 1 quarter, 1 nickel, 2 pennies
B. 3 quarters, 1 dime, 1 nickel, 1 penny
C. one $1 bill, 3 quarters
D. 3 quarters, 2 pennies
E. 3 quarters, 2 dimes, 1 penny
F. one $1 bill, 1 quarter, 1 penny
G. 3 quarters, 1 dime
H. one $1 bill, 2 dimes, 3 pennies

Page 309

A. quarter, nickel
B. half-dollar, 3 dimes
C. NOT ENOUGH
D. NOT ENOUGH
E. half-dollar, 2 dimes, 1 penny
F. NOT ENOUGH

FS-32502 Big Book of Basic S